ESSENTIALS OF SAFETY

General Industry Training and Reference Guide

Volume II

Made with

Use this QR Code to see if you have
the most current edition
or visit www.regqr.com/bk/59471.html

6 88550 00419 0

Copyright © MCMXCVIII - MMXIII
by

315 West Fourth Street
Davenport, Iowa 52801
(563) 323-6245
1-800-MANCOMM
(6 2 6 - 2 6 6 6)
Fax: (563) 323-0804

Website: http://www.mancomm.com
E-mail: safetyinfo@mancomm.com

All rights reserved. Printed in the U.S.A. This publication is intended for instructional and educational use only. This book is meant to provide a formatted and easy-to-understand tool for the reader to train and be trained pursuant to OSHA require- ments for 10- and 30-hour general industry safety training. While these volumes meet and exceed the OSHA requirements, please note that they are not an exhaustive overview of every OSHA topic or regulation. These volumes do not alter or deter- mine compliance responsibilities under Title 29, Code of Federal Regulations Parts 1903, 1904, 1910, and 1926 or the Occupa- tional Safety and Health Act of 1970. Except as permitted under applicable law, no part of this publication may, by the person to whom it is first provided or by any other person(s), be reproduced or distributed in any form or by any means, or stored in any database or other retrieval system, without the prior written permission of the publisher.

This publication is provided as training information in connection with a training course. Although the Federal Regulations published as promulgated are in the public domain, their formatting and sequencing, and other materials contained herein, are subject to copyright law. While best efforts have been made in order to ensure that the information contained herein is as accurate and as complete as possible at the time of printing, the frequency of changes to the regulations makes it impossible to guarantee the completeness and accuracy of the following information. Therefore, MANCOMM and its subsidiaries shall under no circumstances be liable for any damages resulting from the use of or reliance upon this publication. In no event does MAN- COMM or its subsidiaries express or imply any warranties or assume any liabilities whatsoever arising out of the use or inability to use this material. Furthermore, the mention or appearance of any products, services, companies, organizations, or individuals in no way implies endorsement or denouncement of same by MANCOMM or any of its subsidiaries. This publication is constructed in order to provide accurate information in regard to the material included. It is made with the understanding that the publisher is not involved in providing any accounting, legal, or other professional service(s). If legal consultation or other expert advice is required, the services of a professional person should be engaged.

Library of Congress Control Number: 2013942249
ISBN: 1-59959-206-1

Table of Contents

© MCMXCVII - MMXIII by www.mancomm.com

© MCMXCVII - MMXIII by www.mancomm.com

Module Twenty

CFR Workshop

Refer to the "CFR Workshop Worksheet" in your Student Workbook.

Worksheet Instructions

The worksheet found in your Student Notebook contains a list of regulations covered during Level One classes (e.g., Lockout/Tagout, HazCom, etc.)

Find the following requirements:

› Written Programs

› Inspections/Tests

› Training

› Medical Evaluations

Write down the standard number on your worksheet.

Notes

© MCMXCVII - MMXIII by www.mancomm.com

Module Twenty-One

Safety and Health Program

General Guidelines

Employers are encouraged to institute and maintain a program that provides policies, procedures, and practices that recognize and protect their employees from occupational safety and health hazards.

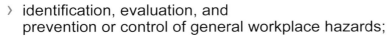

An effective program includes the following that may arise:

› identification, evaluation, and prevention or control of general workplace hazards;

› specific job hazards; and

› potential hazards

Although compliance with the law, including specific OSHA standards, is an important objective, an effective program looks beyond specific requirements of law to address all hazards. It will seek to prevent injuries and illnesses, regardless of whether or not compliance is at issue.

The extent to which the program is described in writing is less important than how effective it is in practice.

OSHA Safety & Health Program
Management Guidelines, Section (a)

Design Standards

Design standards outline the specific details that OSHA requires, such as:
- following specific consensus standards; or
- giving specific dimensions that must be adhered to.

Performance Standards

Performance standards outline the general safety goals OSHA requires, but do not provide specific details.

OSHA's performance standards are flexible so employers can meet these goals by customizing programs according to their facility's needs.

Performance Standards

Requirements listed in the performance standards include:
- training
- recordkeeping
- communicating hazards to employees

Editor's Insight

Documentation

Documentation is required for inspections, accident investigations, and the PPE program.

Examples:
- Small businesses may have some documentation that need not be in writing, provided all employees have the same clear understanding of the policy.

Documentation

Examples: (continued)
- Chemical industry plants producing or using highly hazardous chemicals must be in conformance with the process safety management standard, which involves a lot of documentation.

OSHA Safety & Health Program Management Guidelines, Section (a)

Design Standards

Design standards outline the specific details that OSHA requires, such as:

> following specific consensus standards; or

> giving specific dimensions that must be adhered to.

Performance Standards

Performance standards outline the general safety goals OSHA requires, but do not provide specific details.

OSHA's performance standards are flexible so employers can meet these goals by customizing programs according to their facility's needs.

Requirements listed in the performance standards include:

> training

> recordkeeping

> communicating hazards to employees

Documentation

Documentation is required for inspections, accident investigations, and the PPE program.

Examples:

> Small businesses may have some documentation that need not be in writing, provided all employees have the same clear understanding of the policy.

> Chemical industry plants producing or using highly hazardous chemicals must be in conformance with the process safety management standard, which involves a lot of documentation.

© MCMXCVII - MMXIII by www.mancomm.com

Major Elements

An effective occupational safety and health program will include the following four elements:

1. ## Management commitment and employee involvement

   » Management commitment provides the motivating force and resources for organizing and controlling activities within an organization. Management commitment and employee involvement are essential to a successful safety and health plan.

2. ## Worksite analysis

   » This involves a variety of worksite examinations to identify not only existing hazards but also conditions and operations in which changes might occur that would create hazards.

3. ## Hazard prevention and control

   » Hazard prevention and controls are triggered by a determination that a hazard or potential hazard exists.

   » Where feasible, hazards are prevented by effective design of the jobsite or job.

4. ## Safety and health training

   » Safety and health training addresses the safety and health responsibilities of all personnel concerned with the site, whether salaried or hourly.

   » Safety training is most effective when incorporated into work performance and job-specific training.

OSHA Safety & Health Program Management Guidelines, Section (a)

OSHA Safety & Health Program
Management Guidelines, Section (a)

Recommended Actions

1. **Management commitment and employee involvement**

   » Clearly state a worksite policy on safe and healthful working conditions so all personnel understand the priority of safety and health protection in relation to organizational values.

   » Establish and communicate clear safety goals and objectives for meeting them.

   » Provide visible top management involvement in implementing the program.

   » Provide employee involvement in the structure and operation of the program and in decisions that affect employee safety and health.

   » Assign and communicate responsibility for all aspects of the program.

   » Provide adequate authority and resources to responsible parties so assigned responsibilities can be met.

   » Hold managers, supervisors, and employees accountable for meeting their responsibilities so essential tasks will be performed.

   » Review program operations at least annually to evaluate their success in meeting the goal and objectives.

OSHA Recommendations

Suggested documents to implement management commitment and employee involvement:

› worksite policy (note how this policy is communicated to the workforce and visitors)

› current year's goals, objectives, action plans, and program evaluation

› job descriptions that include safety and health responsibilities

› performance evaluations that include an evaluation of safety and health responsibilities

› budget allocated to safety and health

› contractor bidding proposal sheets showing all contractors' prior safety and health record

› orientation outline for all site visitors, including contractors

› evidence of employee involvement, such as safety committee minutes or other records of employee participation in safety and health program decisions

© MCMXCVII - MMXIII by www.mancomm.com

2. Worksite analysis

» Identify all hazards:

  › Conduct an initial complete worksite survey and periodically update it;

  › Analyze planned and new facilities, processes, materials, and equipment; and

  › Perform routine job hazard analyses.

» Provide for regular site safety and health inspections.

  › Provide and encourage employees to use a system in which they may notify management regarding hazardous conditions and receive timely and appropriate responses so that employee concerns may be addressed without fear of reprisal.

» Provide for investigation of "actual" incidents and "near miss" incidents so causes and means for their prevention are identified.

» Analyze injury and illness trends over time so patterns with common causes can be identified and prevented.

OSHA Safety & Health Program
Management Guidelines, Section (a)

OSHA Recommendations

Suggested documents to implement worksite analysis:

  › results of baseline safety and health surveys with notation of hazard correction
  › forms used for change analyses, including safety and health considerations in the purchase of new equipment, chemical, or materials
  › job hazard analysis
  › employee reports of hazards
  › site safety and health inspection results with hazard corrections noted
  › accident investigation reports with hazard corrections noted
  › trend analyses results

OSHA Safety & Health Program
Management Guidelines, Section (a)

3. Hazard prevention and control

» So all current and potential hazards are corrected or controlled in a timely manner, establish procedures using the following Safety Order of Operations™:

- Engineering controls
- Safe work practices
- Protective equipment

» Provide for facility and equipment maintenance so hazardous breakdown is prevented.

» Plan and prepare for emergencies, and conduct training and drills as needed.

» Establish a medical program that includes availability of first aid, onsite care, and physician and emergency medical care nearby.

OSHA Recommendations

Suggested documents to implement hazard prevention and control:

› preventive maintenance schedule
› disciplinary program and records
› site rules
› written programs mandated by OSHA
› maintenance records
› emergency drill procedures and critiques
› health surveillance and monitoring records
› reports and investigations of near misses, first aid, and OSHA 300 Logs

© MCMXCVII - MMXIII by www.mancomm.com

4. Safety and health training

» Employees:

> › Ensure all employees under-
stand the hazards to which they
may be exposed and how to
protect themselves and others
from exposure to these hazards.

> › Train employees to accept and
follow all safety and health
procedures.

» Supervisors

> › So supervisors will carry out their safety and health responsibili-
ties effectively, ensure that they understand those responsibilities and the reasons for them, including:

>> » analyzing the work under their supervision to identify
unrecognized potential hazards,

>> » maintaining physical protections in their work areas, such as
machine guards, and

>> » reinforcing employee training
on the nature of potential
hazards in their work and on
needed protective measures.

» Managers

> › Ensure managers understand
their safety and health responsibilities so they will effectively
carry out those responsibilities.

™

Safety STOP

OSHA Recommendations

Suggested documents to implement training:
> › list of yearly training topics with the name of the trainer and
his/her qualifications
> › yearly training class schedule with attendance lists
> › individual employee training records with evidence of subject
mastery

**Refer to the "Safety and Health Program Checklist" in your
Student Workbook.**

OSHA Safety & Health Program
Management Guidelines, Section (a)

Notes

© MCMXCVII - MMXIII by www.mancomm.com

Module Twenty-Two

Emergency Action Plan

reg✓SMART™	Emergency Action Plan
Scope	§1910.38(a)
Management Controls	§1910.38
Alerts (postings, signs, markings)	§1910.38(d); Appendix to Subpart E(1)
Records and Procedures	§1910.38(b), (c)
Training	§1910.38(e), (f)

Covers 1910.38

Editor's Insight

Appendix to Subpart E (1)

Disaster Statistics

2002

> 165 workplace deaths occurred due to fires.

2003

> 96 people died in a fast-moving fire at a Rhode Island nightclub.

> A raging storm of tornadoes ran across Tornado Alley. One of the worst tornado outbreaks in recent memory, it killed at least 39 people and obliterated towns in Kansas, Missouri, and Tennessee.

2004

> There were over 1,700 tornadoes in the United States, the most turbulent year in history since records of tornadoes have been kept.

> All 50 states have experienced tornadoes, just some states more often than others.

September 11, 2001

> 3,016 people were killed at the World Trade Center, the Pentagon, and a Pennsylvania field when terrorists attacked the United States.

> However, the death toll at the World Trade Center could have been much higher if it were not for the emergency action plans that were in place that fateful day.

Emergency Action Plan

An emergency action plan is needed to address workplace emergencies that may occur in the workplace, such as:

> fire

> tornadoes

> toxic chemical releases

> hurricanes

> blizzards

> floods

> other emergencies, including bomb threats and terrorists attacks

© MCMXCVII - MMXIII by www.mancomm.com

Who needs training and what type of training would be required?

> Assure an adequate number of trained "evacuation assistants" are available during working hours so that employees can be swiftly moved from the danger location to safe areas.

> One evacuation assistant for each 20 employees in the workplace should be able to provide guidance and instruction during an emergency.

Review the emergency action plan with each employee covered by the plan:

> when the plan is developed;

> when the employee's responsibilities change; and

> when the plan is changed.

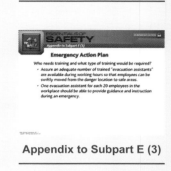

Appendix to Subpart E (3)

OSHA Citation Example

The employer did not review the emergency action plan with each employee covered by the plan when the plan changed.

> At the facility, the emergency action plan underwent revisions that changed the method of notification for a hazardous chemical leak from using the fire alarm to using an announcement over the intercom by the most senior official on duty. However, employees were not retrained.

Appendix to Subpart E (3); §1910.38(f)

> At the facility, the emergency action plan underwent revisions that changed the means of an exit route near the cafeteria area. However, no changes were made to the escape route exit maps, and employees were not retrained.

Type of Violation: Serious

> Proposed Penalty: $4,500.00

§1910.38(f); OSHA Citation

Emergency Action Plan Workshop

Handout: Workplace Map

Using the facility blueprint found in your Student Workbook, identify the following:

> all emergency exits, including the direction of the door swing

>> any required emergency lighting

>> any required eyewashes/emergency showers

> all fire extinguisher locations

> safe areas

Then, thinking about fires or explosions, chemical releases, and severe storms (tornadoes, high winds, etc.), determine the flammable liquid requirements for the following:

> inside storage rooms

> storage cabinets

> fire protection

Justify your answers with a specific regulation (i.e., § 1910.157(d)).

Each workgroup will choose a spokesperson to discuss one area of this facility.

Appendix to Subpart E (non-mandatory)

Posting workplace floor plans that clearly show the emergency escape routes and the use of the color coding will aid employees in determining their exit routes when evacuating the building.

© MCMXCVII - MMXIII by www.mancomm.com

Module Twenty-Three
Sanitation

reg✓SMART™ | Sanitation

Covers 1910.141

Scope	§1910.141(a)(1)
Management Controls	§1910.141
Alerts (postings, signs, markings)	§1910.141(b)(2)(i)
Records and Procedures	
Training	

§1910.141(a)(1), (2)

§1910.141(a)(3)

§1910.141(a)(5)

Sanitation

OSHA's sanitation requirements apply to permanent places of employment.

Definitions:

> **Potable water:** Drinking water

> **Non-potable water:** Water you don't drink

>> ponds, lakes, and streams

>> surface water

>> often used for firefighting

> **Wet process:** Any process in a work area that results in wet ' surfaces where employees may walk or stand

Housekeeping

Keep the workplace:

> clean;

> dry; and

> free from hazards.

If wet processes are used:

> Maintain drainage.

> Provide false floors, platforms, mats, or other dry standing areas or waterproof footwear.

Every enclosed workplace must prevent, as far as reasonably practical, rodents, insects, and other vermin from entering or living in the workplace. If the presence of such vermin is detected, an effective extermination program must be instituted.

© MCMXCVII - MMXIII by www.mancomm.com

Waste Disposal

Containers used for solid or liquid waste must:

> not leak;

> have leak-proof, tight covers, unless the receptacles can be maintained in a sanitary condition without them;

> be cleanable; and

> be emptied on a regular basis to maintain a sanitary workplace.

§1910.141(a)(4)

Eating and Drinking Requirements

Portable drinking water dispensers must be:

> designed, constructed, and serviced so that sanitary conditions are maintained;

> capable of being closed; and

> equipped with a tap.

>> Common drinking cups and other common utensils are prohibited.

>> Open containers are prohibited.

Outlets for non-potable water must be marked to indicate that the water is unsafe and not to be used for drinking, washing of the person, cooking, washing of food, washing of cooking or eating utensils, washing of food preparation or processing premises, washing clothes, or in personal service rooms.

Consumption or storage of food or beverages is not allowed in restrooms or areas exposed to toxic material.

§1910.141(b)(1)

§1910.141(b)(2)(i), (g)(2), (4)

All employee food service facilities and operations must be in accordance with sound hygienic principles. The food dispensed must be wholesome, free from spoilage, and processed, prepared, handled, and stored in a manner that protects against contamination.

§1910.141(h)

ESSENTIALS OF
SAFETY
§1910.141(g)(3)

Sanitation

Eating and Drinking Requirements (continued)
Receptacles for waste food must:
• be constructed of smooth, corrosion-resistant, easily cleanable, or disposable materials;
• be emptied at least once each working day, unless unused;
• be maintained in a clean, sanitary condition; and
• have a solid, tight-fitting cover unless the receptacle can remain sanitary without one.

§1910.141(g)(3)

Receptacles for waste food must:

> be constructed of smooth, corrosion-resistant, easily cleanable, or disposable materials;

> be emptied at least once each working day, unless unused;

> be maintained in a clean, sanitary condition; and

> have a solid, tight-fitting cover unless the receptacle can remain sanitary without one.

Restrooms

Two options:

> separate restrooms for men and women

> a unisex restroom with a lock on the door that will be occupied by no more than one person at a time, and that contains at least one water closet

TM

Best Practice

Responsibilities for cleaning restrooms, washrooms, and the entire facility should be very clearly defined. Dirty facilities make it more likely that people will not help keep them clean or will not use the facilities at all, creating an unsanitary environment. Clean facilities set a good example for everyone. After all, a clean facility can help morale and prevent accidents.

© MCMXCVII - MMXIII by www.mancomm.com

Table J-1	
Number of employees	Minimum number of water closets[a]
1 to 15	1
16 to 35	2
36 to 55	3
56 to 80	4
81 to 110	5
111 to 150	6
Over 150	[b]

a. Where toilet facilities will not be used by women, urinals may be provided instead of toilets, except that the number of toilets shall not be reduced to less than 2/3. Example: 50 men = 2 toilets and 1 urinal.

b. One additional fixture for each additional 40 employees.

Note: These requirements do not apply to mobile crews or to normally unattended work locations so long as employees working at these locations have transportation immediately available to nearby toilet facilities that meet the other OSHA requirements.

Construction of Toilet Rooms

Each toilet shall be provided with a door and walls for privacy.

Lavatories

Each washroom must have:

> hot and cold (or tepid) running water;

> hand soap; and

> individual towels or blowers

Showers

Where showers are required:

> One shower must be provided for each 10 employees of each sex (or fraction thereof) who are required to shower during the same shift.

> Showers must have:

>> body soap,

>> hot and cold water, and

>> individual clean towels.

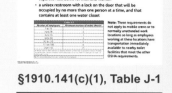

§1910.141(c)(1), Table J-1

§1910.141(c)(2), (d)(2)

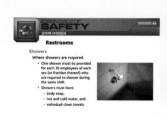

§1910.141(d)(3)

§1910.141(e)

Change Rooms

Whenever employees are required by a particular OSHA standard to wear protective clothing because of the possibility of contamination with toxic materials, change rooms equipped with storage facilities for street clothes and separate storage facilities for the protective clothing shall be provided.

© MCMXCVII - MMXIII by www.mancomm.com

Module Twenty-Four

Signs/Tags

reg✓SMART™	Signs/Tags
Scope	§1910.145(a)(1), (f)(1)
Management Controls	§1910.144; §1910.145
Alerts (postings, signs, markings)	§1910.144(a)(1), (a)(3); §1910.145(c)(1)-(3), (d)(6), (d)(10), (f)(5)-(8)
Records and Procedures	
Training	§1910.145(c)(1)(ii), (c)(2)(ii), (f)(4)(v)

Covers 1910.144; .145

§1910.144(a)(1), (3)

§1910.145(c)(1)

§1910.145(c)(2)

§1910.145(c)(3)

Safety Color Codes

Red is the basic color for:

> fire protection equipment and apparatus

> danger

> safety cans

> stop buttons

> biohazard waste bags, laundry bags, etc.

Yellow is the basic color for:

> caution

> marking physical hazards

Classification of Signs

Danger signs

> All employees shall be instructed that danger signs indicate immediate danger, so special precautions are necessary.

Caution signs

> All employees shall be instructed that caution signs indicate a possible hazard against which proper precaution should be taken.

Safety instruction signs

> Use safety instruction signs where there is a need for general instructions and suggestions relative to safety measures.

Safety instruction signs, when used, shall be white with a green upper panel and white letters to convey the principal message.

Any additional wording on the sign shall be black letters on the white background.

© MCMXCVII - MMXIII by www.mancomm.com

Slow-moving vehicle emblem

> The slow-moving vehicle emblem is to be used on vehicles moving at 25 m.p.h. or less on public roadways. The emblem is not a clearance marker for wide machinery, nor is it intended to replace required lighting or marking of slow-moving vehicles.

Biological hazard signs

> Biological hazard signs are used to signify the actual or potential presence of a biohazard.

Sign Design

Signs must have:

> rounded corners;

> no sharp edges; and

> no bolts sticking out.

All wording on signs must:

> be easy to read and concise;

> provide sufficient information so the sign can be easily understood;

> use a positive, rather than a negative, suggestion; and

> be factually accurate.

OSHA Letter of Interpretation — 07/09/75: Lovested

Symbols on signs used in conjunction with English words meet the requirements of 29 CFR § 1910.145. However, the use of symbol signs without wording would not meet the requirements.

§1910.145(d)(10)

§1910.145(e)(4)

§1910.145(d)(1)

§1910.145(e)(2)

§1910.145(f)(1)(i), (3)

§1910.145(f)(5)

§1910.145(f)(6)

§1910.145(f)(7)

§1910.145(f)(8)

Accident Prevention Tags

Tags are used to prevent accidental injury or illness to employees who are exposed to hazardous or potentially hazardous conditions, equipment, or operations that are out of the ordinary, unexpected, or not readily apparent.

Danger tags shall be used only in major hazard situations were an immediate hazard presents a threat of death or serious injury to employees.

> **Red** with lettering or symbols in a contrasting color is recommended.

Caution tags shall be used only in minor hazard situations where a non-immediate or potential hazards or unsafe practice presents a lesser threat of employee injury.

> **Yellow** with lettering or symbols in a contrasting color is recommended.

Warning tags may be used to represent a hazard level between "Caution" and "Danger."

> **Orange** with lettering and symbols in a contrasting color is recommended.

Biological hazard tags shall be used to identify the actual or potential presence of a biological hazard and to identify equipment, containers, rooms, experimental animals, or combinations thereof, that contain or are contaminated with hazardous biological agents.

> Fluorescent **orange** or **orange-red** with lettering or symbols in a contrasting color is recommended.

Note: A tag's signal word must be readable at a minimum distance of 5 feet. The tag's major message may be presented in pictographs, written text, or both.

Safety STOP™

Best Practice

A lockout/tagout tag must be attached by hand with a non-reusable, self-locking device with a minimum unlocking strength of at least 50 pounds. A nylon cable tie will meet these requirements. Attaching accident prevention tags in the same manner by using a nylon cable tie could eliminate the possibility of improperly attached tags used for lockout/tagout.

© MCMXCVII - MMXIII by www.mancomm.com

Module Twenty-Five

Permit-Required Confined Spaces, Part 2

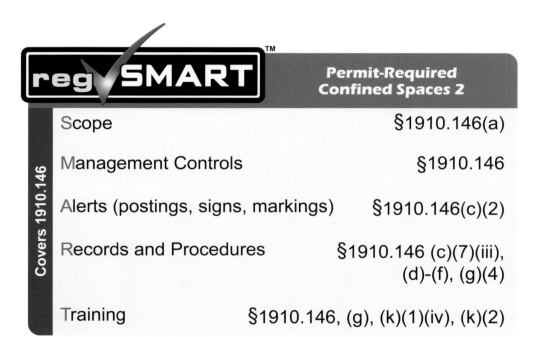

regSMART™

Covers 1910.146

Permit-Required Confined Spaces 2	
Scope	§1910.146(a)
Management Controls	§1910.146
Alerts (postings, signs, markings)	§1910.146(c)(2)
Records and Procedures	§1910.146 (c)(7)(iii), (d)-(f), (g)(4)
Training	§1910.146, (g), (k)(1)(iv), (k)(2)

§1910.146(c)(5)

Alternate Procedures for a Permit Space

An employer may use alternate procedures for entering a permit space if all of the following are true:

› The only hazard posed by the permit space is an actual or potential hazardous atmosphere.

› Continuous forced air ventilation alone is sufficient to maintain the permit space as safe for entry.

› Air monitoring and inspection data shows that the only hazard is due to poor air quality, and forced air ventilation rids the space of this hazard.

» All of this information must be documented to prove the space is safe for entry.

› Employees entering the permit space are trained.

These alternate procedures do not require an entry permit or an attendant, but the person entering the space must be a trained entrant.

Reclassifying a Permit Space

A space classified by the employer as a permit-required confined space may be reclassified as a non-permit confined space under the following procedures:

› The permit space poses no actual or potential atmospheric hazards, and all hazards within the space are eliminated without entry into the space.

› If it is necessary to enter the permit space to eliminate hazards, such entry shall be performed under permit space procedures.

» If testing and inspection during that entry demonstrate that the hazards within the permit space are eliminated, then the space may be reclassified.

» **Note:** Control of atmospheric hazards through forced air ventilation does not constitute elimination of the hazards.

§1910.146(c)(7)

© MCMXCVII - MMXIII by www.mancomm.com

> The basis for determining that all hazards in a permit space have been eliminated must be certified. The certification must contain:
>> the date,
>> the location of the space, and
>> the signature of the person making the determination.
> If hazards arise within a reclassified permit space, each employee shall exit the space.

§1910.146(c)(7)

Permit-Required Confined Space Written Program Requirements

> Prevent unauthorized entry.
> Identify and evaluate hazards.
> Develop and implement the means, procedures, and practices necessary for safe permit space entry operations, including:
>> Specify acceptable entry conditions.
>> Allow authorized entrants to observe monitoring and testing.
>> Isolate the permit space.
>> Eliminate or control atmospheric hazards through purging, interting, flushing, or ventilating.
>> Provide barriers to protect entrants from external hazards.
>> Verify acceptable conditions for entry throughout the duration of authorized entry.
> Provide, maintain, and ensure that employees use the following equipment:
>> testing and monitoring equipment
>> ventilating equipment
>> communications equipment
>> personal protective equipment, if engineering and work practice controls are not sufficient
>> lighting equipment
>> barriers and shields
>> entry/exit equipment, such as ladders

§1910.146(d)

Permit-Required Confined Space Written Program Requirements
• Evaluate permit space conditions, as follows, when entry operations are conducted:
– Test for acceptable entry conditions before entry.
– Test or monitor entry conditions to ensure acceptability during entrance. Test first for oxygen, then for combustible gases and vapors, and then for toxic gases and vapors.

Permit-Required Confined Space Written Program Requirements
– Allow authorized entrants to observe pre-entry and subsequent monitoring or testing.
– Reevaluate the permit space if an entrant believes the evaluation of the space may not have been adequate.
– Immediately provide authorized entrants with testing results.

Permit-Required Confined Space Written Program Requirements
• Provide at least one attendant outside the permit space being entered.
• Specify the means and procedures for an attendant monitoring multiple permit spaces during entry so that the attendant is able to effectively monitor the entries.

Permit-Required Confined Space Written Program Requirements
• Designate those with active roles, identify their duties, and train:
– authorized entrants,
– entrants,
– entry supervisors, and
– those performing testing/monitoring.

Permit-Required Confined Space Written Program Requirements
• Develop and implement rescue and emergency procedures, including:
– how to summon,
– how to rescue attendants,
– how to provide for any necessary emergency services, and
– how to prevent unauthorized personnel from attempting rescue.

§1910.146(d)

» rescue and emergency equipment

» any other necessary equipment

❯ Evaluate permit space conditions, as follows, when entry operations are conducted:

» Test for acceptable entry conditions before entry.

» Test or monitor entry conditions to ensure acceptability during entrance. Test first for oxygen, then for combustible gases and vapors, and then for toxic gases and vapors.

» Allow authorized entrants to observe pre-entry and subsequent monitoring or testing.

» Reevaluate the permit space if an entrant believes the evaluation of the space may not have been adequate.

» Immediately provide authorized entrants with testing results.

❯ Provide at least one attendant outside the permit space being entered.

❯ Specify the means and procedures for an attendant monitoring multiple permit spaces during entry so that the attendant is able to effectively monitor the entries.

❯ Designate those with active roles, identify their duties, and train:

» authorized entrants,

» entrants,

» entry supervisors, and

» those performing testing/monitoring.

❯ Develop and implement rescue and emergency procedures, including:

» how to summon,

» how to rescue attendants,

» how to provide for any necessary emergency services, and

» how to prevent unauthorized personnel from attempting rescue.

© MCMXCVII - MMXIII by www.mancomm.com

> Develop and implement a system for permit procedures, including:
>> preparation,
>> issuance,
>> use, and
>> cancellation.
> Coordinate entry operations with any other employers that have authorized entrants.
> Develop and implement procedures for concluding entry after operations.
> Review entry operations (and revise the program as necessary) when the employer has reason to believe that the measures taken may not protect employees.
> Review the program, using canceled permits, within one year after each entry, revise the program as necessary, and ensure protection.

§1910.146(d)

Discussion

Confined Space Classroom Discussion

> Do you have confined spaces in your facility?
> What about permit-required confined spaces?
> What hazards will be encountered in this confined space?
> Do you need a confined space entry permit for this space?
> Under what conditions could you consider this confined space to be a non-permit confined space?

OSHA Notes

A normal atmosphere is composed approximately of 20.9% oxygen, 78.1% nitrogen, and 1% argon with small amounts of various other gases. Reduction of oxygen in a confined space may be the result of either consumption or displacement.

§1910.146(f)

Permits

In order to enter a permit-required confined space according to the procedures, a written entry permit is required. This permit should contain the following information:

> permit space to be entered

> purpose of the entry

> date and the authorized duration of the entry permit

> authorized entrants within the permit space

> personnel serving as attendants

> entry supervisor

> hazards of the permit space

> measures used to isolate the permit space, as well as eliminate and control hazards

> acceptable entry conditions

> results of initial and periodic monitoring

> rescue and emergency service implementation

> communication procedures between entrant and attendant

> all equipment used in any aspect of the entry

> any additional permits necessary for the work to be completed and other pertinent information

Safety STOP™

OSHA Notes — §1910.146(b)

A permit-required confined space entry supervisor also may serve as an attendant or as an authorized entrant, as long as that person is trained and equipped for each role he or she fills. Also, the duties of entry supervisor may be passed from one individual to another during the course of an entry operation.

Refer to Appendix D-1 and D-2 in your Student Workbook for examples of confined space permits.

© MCMXCVII - MMXIII by www.mancomm.com

Fatality Statistics and Cases

More than 60% of confined space fatalities are would-be rescuers. The following cases demonstrate how testing the atmosphere of the confined space before entry and continual monitoring can prevent such fatalities. In addition, the proper rescue procedures need to be followed in order to eliminate the risk of fatalities.

Case #1:

> Two workers (26 and 27 years old) were overcome by gas vapors and drowned after rescuing a third worker from a fracturing tank at a natural gas well. The tank contained a mixture of mud, water, and natural gas. The first worker had been attempting to move a hose from the tank to another tank. The hose was secured by a chain, and when the worker moved the hose, the chain fell into the tank. The worker entered the tank to retrieve the chain and was overcome.

Case #2:

> A 21-year-old worker died inside of a wastewater holding tank that was 4 feet in diameter and 8 feet deep while attempting to clean and repair a drain line. Sulfuric acid was used to unclog a floor drain leading into the holding tank. The worker collapsed and fell face down into 6 inches of water in the bottom of the tank. A second 21-year-old worker attempted a rescue and was also overcome and collapsed. The first worker was pronounced dead at the scene, and the second worker died two weeks later. The cause of death was attributed to asphyxiation by methane gas. Sulfuric acid vapors also may have contributed to the cause of death.

OSHA Fatal Facts

ESSENTIALS OF
SAFETY
OSHA Fatal Facts

Fatality Statistics and Cases

Case #3:
- A 27-year-old sewer worker entered an underground pumping station (8' x 8' x 7') via a fixed ladder inside a 3-foot diameter shaft. Because the work crew was unaware of procedures to isolate the work area and ensure the pump was bypassed, the transfer line was still under pressure. Therefore, when the workers removed the bolts from an inspection plate that covered a check valve, the force of the wastewater blew the inspection plate off, allowing sewage to flood the chamber, trapping one of the workers. A co-worker, a supervisor, and a police officer attempted a rescue and died. The first two deaths appeared to be due to drowning, and the latter two appeared to be due to asphyxiation as a result of inhalation of "sewer gas."

ESSENTIALS OF
SAFETY
OSHA Fatal Facts

Fatality Statistics and Cases

Case #4:
- A 22-year-old worker died inside a toluene storage tank that was 10 feet in diameter and 20 feet high while attempting to clean the tank. The worker entered the tank through the 16-inch diameter top opening using a 1/2-inch rope for descent. Although a self-contained breathing apparatus was present, the worker was not wearing it when he entered the tank. The worker was overcome and collapsed onto the floor the tank. In an attempt to rescue the worker, fire department personnel began cutting an opening into the side of the tank. The tank exploded, killing a 32-year-old firefighter and injuring 15 others.

OSHA Fatal Facts

Case #3:

A 27-year-old sewer worker entered an underground pumping station (8' x 8' x 7') via a fixed ladder inside a 3-foot diameter shaft. Because the work crew was unaware of procedures to isolate the work area and ensure the pump was bypassed, the transfer line was still under pressure. Therefore, when the workers removed the bolts from an inspection plate that covered a check valve, the  force of the wastewater blew the inspection plate off, allowing sewage to flood the chamber, trapping one of the workers. A co-worker, a supervisor, and a police officer attempted a rescue and died. The first two deaths appeared to be due to drowning, and the latter two appeared to be due to asphyxiation as a result of inhalation of "sewer gas."

Case #4:

A 22-year-old worker died inside a toluene storage tank that was 10 feet in diameter and 20 feet high while attempting to clean the tank. The worker entered the tank through the 16-inch diameter top opening using a 1/2-inch rope for descent. Although a self-contained breathing apparatus was present, the worker was not wearing it when he entered the tank. The worker was overcome and collapsed onto the floor the tank. In an attempt to rescue the worker,  fire department personnel began cutting an opening into the side of the tank. The tank exploded, killing a 32-year-old firefighter and injuring 15 others.

Refer to the "Safe Entry Checklist" in your Student Workbook.
This checklist will help you to ensure that any permit-required confined space you may be required to enter is safe.

© MCMXCVII - MMXIII by www.mancomm.com

Module Twenty-Six
Lockout/Tagout, Part 2

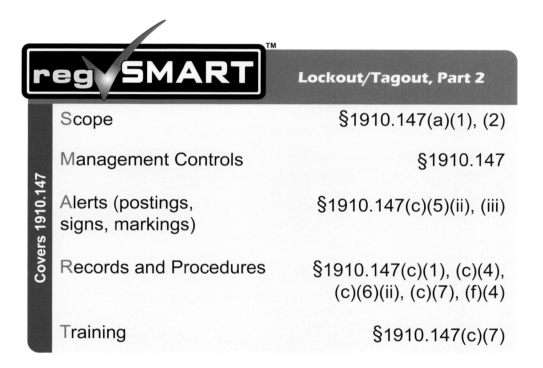

reg✓SMART™	Lockout/Tagout, Part 2
Scope	§1910.147(a)(1), (2)
Management Controls	§1910.147
Alerts (postings, signs, markings)	§1910.147(c)(5)(ii), (iii)
Records and Procedures	§1910.147(c)(1), (c)(4), (c)(6)(ii), (c)(7), (f)(4)
Training	§1910.147(c)(7)

Covers 1910.147

Discussion

See the "Sample Lockout/Tagout Checklist" in your Student Workbook.

OSHA Notes

› Compliance with the Lockout/Tagout Standard prevents an estimated 120 fatalities and 50,000 injuries each year.
› Workers injured on the job from exposure to hazardous energy lose an average of 24 work days for recuperation.

Lockout/Tagout Workshop

Handout: 12 Steps to Lockout/Tagout

› **Equipment:** Large production machine (e.g., plastic siding)

› **Power:** The large production machine uses:

» **Electrical:** (from 2 sources) (less than 600 volts) (Examples: SW #LPME1 and #LPME2)

» **Hydraulic:** 400 psi (Example: Valve #LPMH1)

» **Pneumatic:** 95 psi (Example: Valve #LPMA1)

» **Steam:** 300 psi, 600°F (Example: Valve #LPMS1)

› **Situation:** A contractor is coming in to upgrade the electrical controls. Site employees are going to touch up the painted surfaces, patch the floor, replace some Plexiglas, and generally clean up the area.

› **Challenge:** Answer the following:

» Identify the control methods and devices to be used.

» Identify the training required.

» Identify the necessary communication demands.

» Would this be a good opportunity to do a periodic inspection?

» An employee left the plant and left his lock on a lock box. What do we do?

See the "Typical Minimal Lockout Procedure" in your Student Workbook.

© MCMXCVII - MMXIII by www.mancomm.com

Module Twenty-Seven
Welding/Cutting/ Brazing

reg✔SMART™	**Gas Welding**
Scope	
Management Controls	§1910.252; §1910.253
Alerts (postings, signs, markings)	§1910.252(b)(2)(ii)[G], (b)(4)(vii), (c)(1)(iv); §1910.253(b)(1)(ii), (b)(5)(iii)[G], (c)(3)(v) (d)(4), (e)(6)(iii), (f)(1), (f)(7)(i)[A], (g)(1)(ii)
Records and Procedures	§1910.252(a)(2)(iv), (a)(2)(xiii)[A]; §1910.253(b)(5), (c)(5)
Training	§1910.252(a)(2)(xiii)[C], §1910.253(a)(4)

Covers 1910.252; .253

§1910.252(a)(1);
NFPA Standard 51B

§1910.252(a)(1)

§1910.252(a)(2)(i)

Welding Area Designation

Designated welding areas include:

> areas designated by management

> areas where NO fire hazards are present

> machine shops designed for welding

> weld shops and departments

Non-designated welding areas include:

> areas NOT designated by management

> areas where fire hazards are present

> areas where the object to be welded or cut cannot be moved (in which case, the fire hazards should be removed, or guards must be used)

> areas requiring a hot work permit

Basic Precautions for Hot Work

Fire Hazards

If the object to be welded or cut cannot be moved, all movable fire hazards in the vicinity must be taken to a safe place.

Guards

If the object to be welded or cut cannot be moved and if all the fire hazards cannot be removed, then guards must be used to confine the heat, sparks, and slag to protect employees from the fire hazards.

Special Precautions for Hot Work

Combustible Material

Precautions must be taken so that combustible materials on the floor below will not be exposed to falling sparks.

The same precautions must be observed with regard to walls, open doorways, and open or broken windows.

© MCMXCVII - MMXIII by www.mancomm.com

Fire Extinguishers

Suitable fire-extinguishing equipment must be ready for immediate use.

Fire Watch

Fire watchers are required whenever welding or cutting is performed where more than a minor fire might develop, or any of the following conditions exist:

> Combustible material is closer than 35 feet to the hot work.

> Combustibles are more than 35 feet away, but are easily ignited by sparks.

> Wall or floor openings within a 35-foot radius expose combustible material in adjacent areas, including concealed spaces in walls or floors.

> Combustible materials are adjacent to the opposite side of metal partitions, walls, ceilings, or roofs and are likely to be ignited by conduction or radiation.

Fire watchers must have fire-extinguishing equipment readily available and be trained in its use, as follows.

> They must know how to sound the fire alarm.

> They must watch for fires in all exposed areas.

> They must only try to extinguish fires within the capacity of the firefighting equipment available, or otherwise sound the alarm.

A fire watch must be maintained for at least 30 minutes after completion of welding or cutting to detect and extinguish possible smoldering fires.

Authorization

Before cutting or welding is permitted:

> The authorized individual must inspect the area.

> The individual must designate precautions to be followed, preferably in the form of a written permit.

§1910.252(a)(2)(ii)

§1910.252(a)(2)(iii)

§1910.252(a)(2)(iv)

Special Precautions for Hot Work

Hot Work Permit

The hot work permit should document that the fire prevention and protection requirements have been followed prior to beginning the hot work operations.

It should indicate the following:
- date authorized for hot work
- object on which hot work is to be performed

The permit should be kept on file until completion of the hot work operations.

§1910.252(a)(2)(iv)

Special Precautions for Hot Work

Prohibited areas

Hot work is not permitted in the following situations:
- areas not authorized by management
- sprinkler-equipped buildings while such protection is impaired
- in the presence of explosive atmospheres such as:
  - mixtures of flammable gases, vapors, liquids, or dusts with air

Special Precautions for Hot Work

Prohibited areas (continued)
- tanks or equipment that previously contained flammable materials or dusts, where an explosive atmosphere may develop inside it if improperly cleaned or prepared
- areas that may accumulate combustible dusts
- areas near the storage of large quantities of exposed, readily ignitable materials such as bulk sulfur, baled paper, or cotton

§1910.252(a)(2)(vi)

Special Precautions for Hot Work

Relocation of Combustibles

All combustibles must be relocated at least 35 feet from the worksite.

Where combustibles cannot be relocated, protect them by using:
- flame-proof covers; or
- metal or asbestos guards or curtains.

§1910.252(a)(2)(vii)

Hot Work Permit

The hot work permit should document that the fire prevention and protection requirements have been followed prior to beginning the hot work operations.

It should indicate the following:

> date authorized for hot work

> object on which hot work is to be performed

The permit should be kept on file until completion of the hot work operations.

Note: See the Hot Work Permit in your Student Workbook.

Prohibited areas

Hot work is not permitted in the following situations:

> areas not authorized by management

> sprinkler-equipped buildings while such protection is impaired

> in the presence of explosive atmospheres such as:

>> mixtures of flammable gases, vapors, liquids, or dusts with air

>> tanks or equipment that previously contained flammable materials or dusts, where an explosive atmosphere may develop inside it if improperly cleaned or prepared

>> areas that may accumulate combustible dusts

> areas near the storage of large quantities of exposed, readily ignitable materials such as bulk sulfur, baled paper, or cotton

Relocation of Combustibles

All combustibles must be relocated at least 35 feet from the worksite.

Where combustibles cannot be relocated, protect them by using:

> flame-proof covers; or

> metal or asbestos guards or curtains.

© MCMXCVII - MMXIII by www.mancomm.com

Management

Management is responsible for the safe usage of cutting and welding equipment on its property.

Based on fire potentials of plant facilities, management must:

> establish areas for cutting and welding;

> establish procedures for cutting and welding in other areas;

> designate an individual responsible for authorizing cutting and welding operations in these areas;

> insist that cutters or welders and their supervisors are suitably trained in the safe operation of their equipment; and

> advise all contractors about flammable materials or hazardous conditions they may not be aware of.

Supervisors

Supervisors are responsible for the safe handling of equipment and the safe use of cutting or welding processes. Supervisors must:

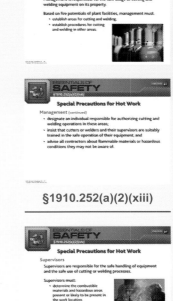

> determine the combustible materials and hazardous areas present or likely to be present in the work location;

> protect combustibles from ignition by the following:

>> Move the work to a location free from dangerous combustibles.

>> If the work cannot be moved, move the combustibles to a safe distance, or have the combustibles properly shielded against ignition.

>> See that hot work is scheduled so plant operations that might expose combustibles to ignition are not started during cutting or welding operations.

> secure authorization for the hot work from the designated management representative;

> determine if the cutter or welder secures approval that conditions are safe before hot work begins;

> determine that fire-extinguishing equipment is located at the; and

> see that fire watchers are available at the site when required.

§1910.252(a)(2)(xiii)

§1910.252(a)(2)(xiv)

OSHA Fatal Facts

§1910.252(a)(3)

§1910.252(c)(13)

Welding Accident

Brief Description of the Accident

Two employees were welding brackets onto an oil storage tank (55,000 gallons). The tank, half full, contained explosive atmospheres of vapor from waste chemical and oil materials from automobile and truck service stations. One worker was killed and the other injured when the tank exploded and the top was blown off.

Inspection Results

As a result of its investigation, OSHA issued citations for violations of four standards.

This is Why...

Welding, cutting, or other hot work must NOT be performed on used drums, barrels, tanks, or other containers unless they have been cleaned so thoroughly as to make absolutely certain that there are no flammable materials present.

Any pipe lines or connections to the drum or vessel must be disconnected or blanked.

First Aid

- › First-aid equipment must be available at all times.
- › All injuries must be reported as soon as possible for medical attention.
- › First-aid treatment must be rendered until medical attention can be provided.

© MCMXCVII - MMXIII by www.mancomm.com

Hot Work in Confined Spaces

Accidental Contact with Arc Welding Equipment

When arc welding is suspended for any substantial period of time, such as during lunch or overnight, all electrodes must be removed from the holders and the holders located so that accidental contact cannot occur, and the machine must be disconnected from the power source.

Torch Valve for Gas Welding

In order to eliminate the possibility of gas escaping through leaks or improperly closed valves, the torch valves must be closed and the gas supply shut off outside the confined area whenever the torch is not to be used for a substantial period of time.

The torch and hose must also be removed from the confined space.

Gas Cylinders and Welding Machines

When welding or cutting is being performed in any confined space, gas cylinders and welding machines must be left outside the space.

Lifelines

Where a welder must enter a confined space through a manhole or other small opening, means must be provided for quickly removing the welder in case of emergency.

Safety belts and lifelines may be used for this purpose. They must be attached to the welder's body so the welder cannot be jammed in a small exit opening.

An attendant with a pre-planned rescue procedure must be stationed outside to observe the welder at all times and be capable of putting rescue operations into effect.

§1910.252(a)(4)(i)

§1910.252(a)(4)(ii)

§1910.252(b)(4)(iii)

§1910.252(b)(4)(iv)

Protection of Personnel

§1910.252(b)(1)(i)

§1910.252(b)(2)

Protection from Falling

A welder or helper working on platforms, scaffolds, or runways must be protected against falling.

This may be accomplished by the use of the following:

> railings

> safety belts

> life lines

> other equally effective safeguards

Safety STOP™

OSHA Letter of Interpretation — 02/18/99: Claypool

A restraint system consists of a body belt or harness, lanyard, and anchor. The system is arranged so that the worker is prevented from falling any distance. A system that exposes a worker to a fall, but stops the fall within specified parameters, is a personal fall arrest system.

Eye Protection

Helmets or hand shields must be used during all arc welding or arc cutting operations, excluding submerged arc welding.

Helpers and attendants must also be provided with proper eye protection.

Goggles or other suitable eye protection must be used during all gas welding or oxygen cutting operations.

Glasses with suitable filter lenses are permitted for use during gas welding operations on light work, torch brazing, or inspection.

Transparent face shields or goggles must be used by all operators and attendants of resistance welding or resistance brazing equipment, depending on the particular job, to protect their faces or eyes as required.

© MCMXCVII - MMXIII by www.mancomm.com

Protective Clothing

Welders, cutter, and brazers must also wear protective clothing if necessary. Choice will vary with the size, nature, and location of the work to be performed.

Health Protection and Ventilation

The following three factors in arc and gas welding govern the amount of contamination to which welders may be exposed:

> dimensions of space in which welding is to be done with special regard to height of ceiling

> number of welders

> possible evolution of hazardous fumes, gases, or dust according to the metals involved

If welding must be performed in a space entirely screened on all sides, the screens must be arranged so that they do not restrict ventilation. If possible, mount the screens so that they are approximately 2 feet above the floor, unless the work is being performed so low that the screen must be extended nearer to the floor to protect nearby workers from the welding glare.

Local exhaust or general ventilation must be used to keep the amount of toxic fumes, gases, or dusts below the maximum alloweable concentration as specified in §1910.1000.

§1910.252(b)(3)

§1910.252(c)(1)(i)

Health Protection and Ventilation

§1910.252(c)(1)(i), (ii)

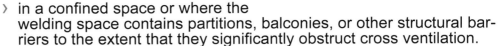

Ventilation for General Welding and Cutting

Mechanical ventilation shall be provided when welding or cutting is done on metals that do not have special ventilation requirements when that welding or cutting is performed:

> in a space of less than 10,000 cubic feet per welder;

> in a room having a ceiling height of less than 16 feet; or

> in a confined space or where the welding space contains partitions, balconies, or other structural barriers to the extent that they significantly obstruct cross ventilation.

If these restrictions do not apply, then natural ventilation is considered sufficient for welding or cutting operations.

Mechanical ventilation must be at least 2,000 cubic feet per minute per welder unless one of the following is used:

> local exhaust hoods or booths

> airline respirators

§1910.252(c)(2); ANSI Z49.1d

Hoods

§1910.252(c)(3)(i)

Welding Zone	Duct Diameter, Inches[2]	Minimum air flow[1] cubic ft/min.
4 to 6 inches from arc or torch	3	150
6 to 8 inches from arc or torch	3 ½	275
8 to 10 inches from arc or torch	4 ½	425
10 to 12 inches from arc or torch	5 ½	600

1. When brazing with cadmium-bearing materials or when cutting on such materials, increased rates of ventilation may be required.

2. Nearest half-inch duct diameter based on 4,000 feet per minute velocity in pipe.

© MCMXCVII - MMXIII by www.mancomm.com

Ventilation in Confined Spaces

All welding and cutting operations in confined spaces must be ventilated to prevent the accumulation of toxic material or possible oxygen deficiency.

> This applies not only to the welder but also to helpers and other personnel in the immediate vicinity.

All replacement air must be clean and breathable.

> Oxygen must never be used for ventilation.

If it is impossible to provide the required ventilation, NIOSH-approved airline respirators or hose masks must be used. (**Note:** If hose masks, hose masks with blowers, or self-contained breathing equipment is used, a worker must be stationed on the outside of the confined space to ensure the safety of those working inside.)

In areas that are immediately hazardous to life, one of the following must be used:

> a full-facepiece, pressure-demand, self-contained breathing apparatus

> a combination full-facepiece, pressure-demand, supplied-air respirator with an auxiliary, self-contained, NIOSH-approved air supply

§1910.252(c)(4)

§1910.252(c)(4)(iii)

§1910.252(c)(5)-(12)

OSHA Notes

The following list identifies chemicals commonly associated with welding, cutting, and brazing operations:

› Metals: The metals that may be present will depend on the material being worked on and the makeup of welding rods, fluxes, etc. For specific information, see the appropriate Safety Data Sheets.
  » Aluminum, Antimony, Arsenic, Beryllium, Cadmium, Chromium, Chromium hexavalent, Cobalt, Copper, Iron, Lead, Manganese, Molybdenum, Nickel, Silver, Tin, Titanium, Vanadium, Zinc
› Other chemicals: These are present in the fluxes used or may be produced by the welding operation.
  » Carbon dioxide, Carbon monoxide, Fluoride, Nitrogen dioxide, Nitric oxide, Ozone, Particulates
› Decomposition products: These will vary depending on the presence of coatings that may be on or near the object being welded. Residues left by degreasing, usually chlorinated hydrocarbons, may form these compounds when heated.
  » Acetaldehyde, Acrolein, Carbonyl fluoride, Chloroacetic acid, Formaldehyde, Hydrogen chloride, Hydrogen fluoride, Perfluoroisobutylene, Phosgene, Phosphine

The following compounds have special ventilation requirements:

F	Fluorine compounds	§1910.252(c)(5)
Zn	Zinc	§1910.252(c)(6)
Pb	Lead	§1910.252(c)(7)
Be	Beryllium	§1910.252(c)(8)
Cd	Cadmium	§1910.252(c)(9)
Hg	Mercury	§1910.252(c)(10)
	Cleaning compounds	§1910.252(c)(11)
	Stainless steels	§1910.252(c)(12)

© MCMXCVII - MMXIII by www.mancomm.com

Welding Equipment

General Oxygen/Acetylene Equipment Safety

Follow these requirements:

> Empty cylinders must have their valves closed.

> Where a cylinder is designed to accept a valve protection cap, the cap must always be in place and hand-tight, except when cylinders are in use or connected for use.

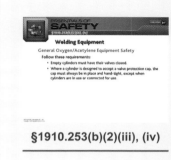

§1910.253(b)(2)(iii), (iv)

> When parallel lengths of oxygen and acetylene hose are taped together for convenience and to prevent tangling, not more than 4 inches out of 12 inches may be covered by tape.

> Hose showing leaks, burns, worn places, or other defects rendering it unfit for service must be repaired or replaced.

> Cylinders inside of buildings must be stored:

>> at least 20 feet from highly combustible materials such as oil or wood chips,

§1910.253(e)(5)(ii), (v)

>> in a location that is:

>>> well-protected,

>>> well ventilated, and

>>> dry,

>> away from elevators, stairs, or gangways,

>> in assigned storage spaces where cylinders will not be:

>>> knocked over,

>>> damaged by passing or falling objects, or

>>> subject to tampering by unauthorized persons, and

>> in ventilated enclosures, not in lockers or cupboards that are unventilated.

§1910.253(b)(2)(ii)

§1910.253(b)(4)(iii)

Arc Welding

Scope

Management Controls
§1910.251, §1910.255

Alerts
§1910.254(b)(4)(iv)

Records and Procedures
§1910.255(e)

Training
§1910.254(a)(3), (d)(1); §1910.255(a)(3)

Safety STOP™

OSHA Letter of Interpretation — 12/31/98: Dineen

When is a gas cylinder considered to be "in storage"?

> We consider a cylinder to be in storage when it is reasonably anticipated that gas will not be drawn from the cylinder within 24 hours (overnight hours included). When a cylinder is in storage, the valve cap must be in place and hand-tight.

Oxygen cylinders in storage:

> must be separated from fuel-gas cylinders or combustible materials (especially oil or grease) a minimum distance of 20 feet; or

> by a noncombustible barrier at least 5 feet high having a fire-resistance rating of at least a half hour.

reg✔SMART™	Arc Welding
Scope	
Management Controls	§1910.251; §1910.255
Alerts (postings, signs, markings)	§1910.254(b)(4)(iv)
Records and Procedures	§1910.255(e)
Training	§1910.254(a)(3), (d)(1); §1910.255(a)(3)

Covers 1910.254; .255

© MCMXCVII - MMXIII by www.mancomm.com

Arc Welding

Training

Workers designated to operate arc welding equipment must have gone through proper instruction and be qualified to operate such equipment.

Operation and Maintenance

Grounding: Grounding of the welding machine frame must be checked. Special attention must be given to safety ground connections of portable machines.

Manufacturers' Instructions: Printed rules and instructions covering operation of equipment supplied by the manufacturers must be strictly followed.

Electrode Holders: Electrode holders, when not in use, must be placed so they cannot make electrical contact with persons, conducting objects, fuel, or compressed gas tanks.

Electric Shock: Cables with splices within 10 feet of the holder must not be used. The welder should not coil or loop welding electrode cable around parts of his or her body.

Defective Equipment: The operator should report any equipment defect or safety hazard to his or her supervisor. The use of the equipment must be discontinued until its safety is assured. Only qualified personnel can repair equipment.

> **Note:** Excessive noise is a known health hazard. Air carbon arc cutting and plasma arc cutting are examples of processes that are frequently noisy. Therefore, hearing conservation may be needed.

§1910.254(a)(3)

§1910.254(d)(3), (6)

§1910.254(d)(7), (8)

§1910.254(d)(9)(i)

Notes

© MCMXCVII - MMXIII by www.mancomm.com

Module Twenty-Eight

Hand and Portable Power Tools

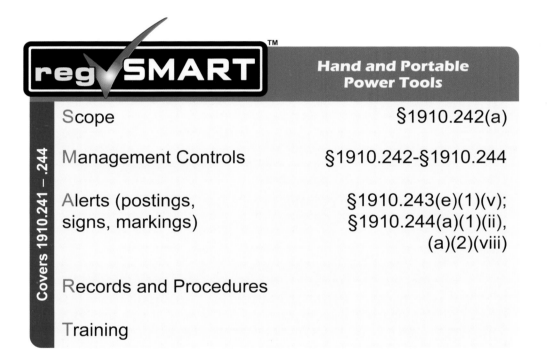

reg✔SMART™	Hand and Portable Power Tools
Scope	§1910.242(a)
Management Controls	§1910.242-§1910.244
Alerts (postings, signs, markings)	§1910.243(e)(1)(v); §1910.244(a)(1)(ii), (a)(2)(viii)
Records and Procedures	
Training	

Covers 1910.241 – .244

Hand Tools

§1910.242(b)

§1910.242(a)

Safety STOP ™

OSHA Notes

The greatest hazards posed by hand tools result from misuse and improper maintenance. Some examples include the following:

› If a chisel is used as a screwdriver, the tip of the chisel may break and fly off, hitting the user or other employees.

› If a wooden handle on a tool, such as a hammer or an axe, is loose, splintered, or cracked, the head of the tool may fly off and strike the user or other employees.

› If the jaws of a wrench are sprung, the wrench might slip.

› If impact tools such as chisels, wedges, or drift pins have mushroomed heads, the heads might shatter on impact, sending sharp fragments flying toward the user or other employees.

Compressed Air

Compressed air shall not be used for cleaning purposes except where:

› reduced to less than 30 p.s.i.; and

› only with effective chip guarding and personal protective equipment.

Safety STOP ™

OSHA Letter of Interpretation — 07/27/79: Barnett

The only restriction on air pressure is that on dead-ending the exit orifice, the static pressure shall be less than 30 p.s.i. The "less than 30 p.s.i." is not to be interpreted as the velocity pressure downstream of the orifice's exit.

Power Tool Requirements

General Requirements

The employer is responsible for the condition of all tools, including employee -owned tools.

© MCMXCVII - MMXIII by www.mancomm.com

Safety STOP™

OSHA Notes

Power Tool Safety Rules

› Never carry a tool by the cord or hose.
› Never yank the cord or the hose to disconnect it from the receptacle.
› Keep cords and hoses away from heat, oil, and sharp edges.
› Disconnect tools when not using them, before servicing and cleaning them, and when changing accessories such as blades, bits, and cutters.
› Keep all people not involved with the work at a safe distance from the work area.
› Secure work with clamps or a vise, freeing both hands to operate the tool.
› Avoid accidental starting. Do not hold fingers on the switch button while carrying a plugged-in tool.
› Maintain tools with care; keep them sharp and clean for best performance.
› Follow instructions in the user's manual for lubricating and
› changing accessories.
› Be sure to keep good footing and maintain good balance when operating power tools.
› Wear proper apparel for the task. Loose clothing, ties, or jewelry can become caught in moving parts.
› Remove all damaged portable electric tools from use and tag them "Do Not Use."
› Never use a tool without its safety guards.
› Never sharpen or tension a blade or cutter unless you have been properly trained to do so.
› Always use eye protection; use hearing, head, hand, and respiratory protection if needed.

§1910.243(a)(2)

§1910.243(a)(2)(i)

Switches and Controls

The following shall be equipped with a constant-pressure switch or control that will shut off the power when the pressure is released:

› all hand-held powered circular saws

› electric, hydraulic, or pneumatic chain saws

› percussion tools

§1910.243(a)(2)(ii)

§1910.243(a)(3), (4)

§§1910.243(a)(5);
.304(g)(6)(vi), (vii)

§1910.243(c)(1)(ii)[a]

All hand-held, gasoline-powered chain saws shall be equipped with a constant-pressure throttle control that will shut off the power to the saw chain when the pressure is released.

The following equipment needs a constant pressure switch or a turnoff switch that uses the same finger that turned the tool on:

> all hand-held powered drills; tappers; fastener drivers; horizontal, vertical, and angle grinders; disc sanders; belt sanders; reciprocating saws; saber, scroll, and jig saws; and other similarly operated power tools

Portable Belt Sanding Machines

Belt sanding machines must be provided with guards at each nip point where the sanding belt runs onto a pulley.

Cracked Saws

All cracked saws must be removed from service.

Jammed Guards

"Suicide rig" jamming or wedging of guards is prohibited.

Grounding

Portable electric powered tools must meet the electrical requirements of Subpart S.

Equipment connected by cord and plug, where the equipment may become energized, shall be grounded or marked as double insulated.

Portable Abrasive Wheels

Portable grinders must have a safety guard to cover the following:

> spindle end

> nut

> flange projections

© MCMXCVII - MMXIII by www.mancomm.com

Inspection and Installation of Abrasive Wheels

Immediately before installing, all abrasive wheels over 2 inches in diameter must be closely inspected and sounded by the user to make sure they have not been damaged in transit, storage, or otherwise.

> For ring test instructions, see the "Abrasive Wheel Machinery" subsection of Module 17 of this text, or §1910.215(d)(1) of the OSHA regulations.

> The spindle speed of the machine shall be checked before installing the wheel to be certain it does not exceed the maximum speed marked on the abrasive wheel.

Excluded Machinery:

The following are excluded from these requirements:

> natural sandstone wheels

> metal, wooden, cloth, or paper discs having a layer of abrasive on the surface

§1910.243(c)(5)(i)

Additional Requirements

Follow these additional requirements for grinders:

> Safety guards for bench and floor stands should not expose the grinding wheel. The distance between the wheel and guard may not exceed 1/4 inch.

> Machines designed for a fixed location must be securely anchored to prevent movement in normal operations.

> An adjustable work-rest of rigid construction must be used to support the work. The work-rest must be kept adjusted closely to the wheel with a maximum clearance of 1/8 inch.

> If employee exposure exceeds the permissible exposure limit, a local exhaust ventilation system with a hood must be used.

> Safety guards on right-angle-head or vertical portable grinders must have a maximum exposure angle of 180°. Guards must be located between the operator and the wheel during use. Adjustments of the guard must cause pieces of a broken wheel to be deflected away from the operator.

§1910.243(c)(6)

§1910.212(b); .215; .243(c)

§1910.243(d)(4)(i)

§1910.243(d)(4)

OSHA Fatal Facts

Explosive-Actuated Fastening Tools

Before using an explosive-actuated fastening tool, inspect it to determine that:

> it is clean;

> all moving parts operate freely; and

> the barrel is free from obstructions.

Nail Gun Safety

Follow these rules for nail guns:

> Do NOT load until just prior to the intended firing time.

> Neither loaded nor empty nail guns should be pointed at any worker.

> Do NOT leave an unattended nail gun loaded.

> Do NOT use an explosive-actuated tool in flammable or explosive atmospheres.

> In case of a misfire, the operator must:

>> Hold the nail gun in the operating position for at least 30 seconds.

>> Then try to operate the nail gun a second time.

>> Wait another 30 seconds, holding the nail gun in the operating position.

>> Proceed to remove the explosive load in strict accordance with the manufacturer's instructions.

Nail Gun Accident

> Brief Description of the Incident:

Two employees doing remodeling construction were building a wall. One worker was killed when he was struck by a nail fired from a powder-actuated tool. The tool operator, while attempting to anchor plywood to a 2"× 4" stud, fired the tool. The nail penetrated the stud and the plywood partition prior to striking the victim.

© MCMXCVII - MMXIII by www.mancomm.com

› Inspection Results:

As a result of its investigation, OSHA issued citations for three serious violations and determined that if employees were trained in the use of powder-actuated tools and precautions were taken to prevent the nail from passing through the wall, the accident probably would not have occurred.

 ™

Best Practice

To prevent hazards associated with the use of nail guns, workers should observe the following general precautions:
› Follow all manufacturer's instructions as well as ANSI A10.3, Safety Requirements for Explosive-Actuated Fastening Tools.
› Personnel who operate powder-actuated tools must be properly trained in their use and carry a valid operator's card provided by the equipment manufacturer.
› A sign at least 7" x 10" with bold-face type reading, "POWDER-ACTUATED TOOL IN USE," must be conspicuously posted when the tool is being used.
› Do not fire fasteners into material that would let them pass through to the other side. Take whatever time is necessary to examine both the surface and the opposite side, assuring your safety as well as the safety of others.
› All powder-actuated tool operators must have and use appropriate personal protective equipment such as hard hats, safety goggles, safety shoes, and ear protectors.

See the "Hazard Alert -- Nail Guns" handout in your Student Workbook.

Power Lawnmowers

Walk-behind, riding-rotary, and reel power lawnmowers must be guarded according to the machine guarding requirements (see §1910.212, General Requirements for All Machines, and Module 17 of this Training and Reference Guide).

General Requirements

A shutoff device must be provided to stop operation of the motor or engine.

› This device must require manual and intentional reactivation to restart the motor or engine.

OSHA Fatal Facts

§1910.243(e)(1)(i)

§1910.243(e)(1)(iii)

§1910.243(e)(1)(v)

§1910.243(e)(2)(v)

§1910.243(e)(2)(i)-(iii)

§1910.244(a)(2)(i)-(iv)

Self-Propelled Lawnmowers

A self-propelled lawnmower needs a clearly visible label at an engine starting control point with the words, "Caution. Be sure the operating controls are in neutral before starting the engine."

Walk-Behind and Riding Rotary Lawnmowers

Place a label on the mower with the word "Caution" or "Danger" at or near each discharge opening.

If the guard must be removed to install a catcher assembly, the mower must:

> have warning instructions near the opening stating that the mower may not be used without either the catcher assembly or the guard in place;

> have had either the catcher assembly or the guard shipped and sold as part of the mower; and

> have an instruction manual stating that the mower may not be used without either the catcher assembly or the guard in place.

Jacks

The jack's rated load must be legibly and permanently marked.

When operating a jack:

> Block the base of the jack if the foundation is not firm.

> Place a block between the cap and the load if it is possible that the cap will slip.

> Do not overrun the indicated stop limit.

> Crib, block, or otherwise secure the load as soon as it has been raised.

> Ensure adequate antifreeze liquid in hydraulic jacks exposed to freezing temperatures.

© MCMXCVII - MMXIII by www.mancomm.com

> Thoroughly inspect jacks no less frequently than:

  » once every 6 months, for constant or intermittent use at one locality,

  » when sent out and when returned, for jacks sent out of the shop for special work, and

  » immediately before and immediately thereafter, for a jack subjected to an abnormal load or shock.

> Tag jacks that are out of order accordingly. Do not use again until repairs are made. Examine repair or replacement parts for possible defects.

§1910.244(a)(2)(iv), (viii)

Notes

© MCMXCVII - MMXIII by www.mancomm.com

Module Twenty-Nine

Electrical Personal Protective Equipment

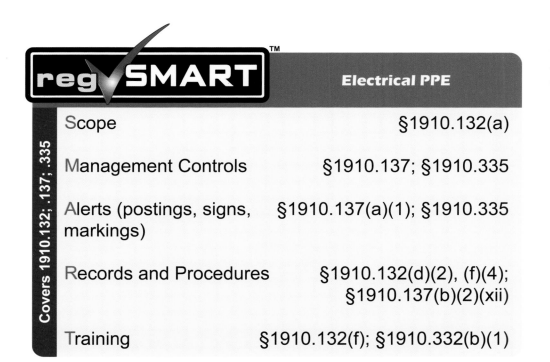

regSMART™	Electrical PPE
Scope	§1910.132(a)
Management Controls	§1910.137; §1910.335
Alerts (postings, signs, markings)	§1910.137(a)(1); §1910.335
Records and Procedures	§1910.132(d)(2), (f)(4); §1910.137(b)(2)(xii)
Training	§1910.132(f); §1910.332(b)(1)

Covers 1910.132; .137; .335

Electrical Protective Devices

See Subpart I Appendix B, Non-Mandatory Compliance Guidelines for Hazard Assessment and Personal Protective Equipment Selection, for compliance assistance for employers and employees in implementing requirements for a hazard assessment and the selection of PPE.

Electrical Protective Devices

When exposed to electrical hazards, each affected employee shall use electrical protective equipment such as:
- insulating blankets
- matting
- covers
- line hose
- gloves
- sleeves made of rubber

Electrical Protective Devices

Equipment markings	Maximum use voltage
Class 00	500 volts
Class 0	1,000 volts
Class 1	7,500 volts
Class 2	17,000 volts
Class 3	26,500 volts
Class 4	36,000 volts

See 29 CFR §1910.137, Tables I-2 through I-6 for proof-test requirements.

§1910.137

Electrical Protective Devices

See Subpart I Appendix B, Non-Mandatory Compliance Guidelines for Hazard Assessment and Personal Protective Equipment Selection, for compliance assistance for employers and employees in implementing requirements for a hazard assessment and the selection of PPE.

When exposed to electrical hazards, each affected employee shall use electrical protective equipment such as:

> insulating blankets

> matting

> covers

> line hose

> gloves

> sleeves made of rubber

Equipment markings	Maximum use voltage[1]
Class 00	500 volts
Class 0	1,000 volts
Class 1	7,500 volts
Class 2	17,000 volts
Class 3	26,500 volts
Class 4	36,000 volts

See 29 CFR §1910.137, Tables I-2 through I-6, for proof-test requirements.

1. Reference NFPA-70E

OSHA Letter of Interpretation–08/12/94: Dittmer:

OSHA will cite at most a de minimis violation to an employer who uses Class 00 rubber insulating gloves that meet the amended ASTM D130 standard.

OSHA Facts

> Electrocution is one of the leading causes of death in the workplace, consistently ranking in the top five causes of workplace deaths.
> Workers under 25 years of age have the highest rate of death from electrocution.

© MCMXCVII - MMXIII by www.mancomm.com

Electrocution

Electrocution results when a human is exposed to a lethal amount of electrical energy.

> For death to occur, the human body must become part of an active electrical circuit having a current capable of over-stimulating the nervous system or causing damage to internal organs.

> The extent of injuries received depends on:

>> the current's magnitude,

>> the pathway of the current through the body, and

>> the duration of the current flow through the body.

A common fuse or breaker opens a circuit at 15 – 20 amps. However, the estimated effect on humans is as follows:

60 Hz AC currents	Human effect
1 mA	Barely perceptible
16 mA	Maximum current an average human can grasp and "let go"
20 mA	Paralysis of respiratory muscles
100 mA	Ventricular fibrillation threshold
2 Amps	Cardiac standstill and internal organ damage

The presence of moisture from environmental conditions such as standing water, wet clothing, high humidity, or perspiration increases the possibility of electrocution.

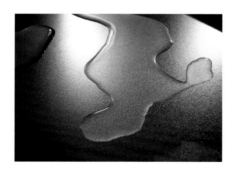

Under dry conditions, the resistance offered by the human body may be as high as 100,000 ohms. Wet or broken skin may drop the body's resistance to 1,000 ohms.

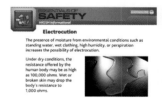

NIOSH Informational

Editor's Insight

§1910.137(b)(1), (2)(ii)

§1910.137(b)(2)(iii)

Ohm's Law

$$Current = \frac{Volts}{Ohms}$$

Low-Voltage Electrocution

> Under dry conditions:
>> 120 volts / 100,000 ohms = 1 mA
>>> Barely perceptible level of current
> Under wet conditions:
>> 120 volts / 1,000 ohms = 120 mA
>>> Sufficient current to cause ventricular fibrillation

Best Practice

Remember that an electrical hazard becomes much more dangerous in damp or wet conditions. Even if you do not see water, assume there may be dampness in any work location. After all, even sweat can create a damp condition!

In-Service Care and Use

Electrical protective equipment shall be maintained in a safe, reliable condition.

Inspections

Inspect electrical protective equipment as follows:

> Insulating equipment shall be inspected for damage before each day's use and immediately following any incident that can reasonably be suspected of having caused damage.
> Insulating gloves shall be given an air test along with an inspection.

© MCMXCVII - MMXIII by www.mancomm.com

› Insulating equipment with any of the following defects may not be used:

» a hole, tear, puncture, or cut

» ozone cutting or ozone checking, which is the cutting action produced by ozone on rubber under mechanical stress into a series of interlacing cracks

» an embedded foreign object

» a change in texture such as swelling, softening, hardening, or becoming sticky or inelastic

» any other defect that damages the insulating properties

§1910.137(b)(2)(iv)

Maintenance of Insulating Equipment

Insulating equipment found to have other defects that might affect its insulating properties shall be removed from service and returned for testing.

Insulating equipment shall be cleaned as needed to remove foreign substances.

Insulating equipment shall be stored in a location so as to protect it from light, temperature extremes, excessive humidity, ozone, and other injurious substances or conditions.

§1910.137(b)(2)(v), (vi)

Protector Gloves

Protector gloves shall be worn over insulating gloves.

› **Exception:** Protector gloves need not be used with Class 0 gloves under limited-use conditions where small equipment and parts manipulation necessitate unusually high finger dexterity.

§1910.137(b)(2)(vii)

Testing Requirements

Electrical protective equipment shall be subjected to periodic electrical tests.

Test voltages and the maximum intervals between tests shall be in accordance with Table I-5 and Table I-6.

§1910.137(b)(2)(viii)

§1910.137(b)(2)(ix)-(xi)

§1910.137(b)(2)(xii)

Standard Electrical Test Methods	
Consensus Standard	**Description**
ASTM D 120-87	Specification for Rubber Insulating Gloves
ASTM D 1048-93	Specification for Rubber Insulating Blankets
ASTM D 1049-93	Specification for rubber Insulating Covers
ASTM D 1050-90	Specification for Rubber Insulating Line Hose
ASTM D 1051-87	Specification for Rubber Insulating Sleeves
ASTM F 478-92	Specification for In-Service Care of Insulating Line Hose and Covers
ASTM F 479-93	Specification for In-Service Care of Insulating Blankets
ASTM 496-93b	Specification for In-Service Care of Insulating Gloves and Sleeves

Insulating equipment failing to pass inspections or electrical tests may not be used by employees, except as follows:

> Rubber insulating line hoses may be used in shorter lengths with the defective portion cut off.

> Rubber insulating blankets and gloves may be repaired using a compatible patch that results in equal physical and electrical properties of the blanket or gloves.

> The defective piece of a blanket may be severed from the blanket.

Repaired insulating equipment shall be retested before it may be used by employees.

Certification of Equipment Testing

The employer shall certify that electrically protective equipment was tested.

The certification shall identify that the equipment passed the test and the date it was tested.

Note: Two acceptable means of meeting this requirement are:

> marking the electrical protective equipment with the results and the date; and

> entering into a log the results of the tests and the dates of testing.

© MCMXCVII - MMXIII by www.mancomm.com

Conclusion

Remember:

> Electrical hazards represent a serious, widespread occupational danger.

> Practically all members of the workforce are exposed to electrical energy during the performance of their daily duties, and electrocutions occur to workers in various job categories.

> Many workers are unaware of the potential electrical hazards present in their work environment that make them more vulnerable to the danger of electrocution.

Thoughts to ponder for tomorrow's open forum:

A. Do you have workplace issues?

B. Then think about these questions for the open forum:

1. How can we convince employees to become involved in safety?

2. How can we attain management's commitment toward safety?

3. How do we get supervisors to be responsible for safety?

4. How can we change employee or management behavior toward safety?

5. How well do safety incentive programs work?

6. How can we effectively discipline our employees?

7. What affect does reverse psychology have on employees or management in getting them more involved or committed to safety?

8. How can we effectively train our employees?

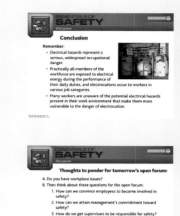

Discussion

Notes

© MCMXCVII - MMXII by www.mancomm.com

Module Thirty
DOT Placarding

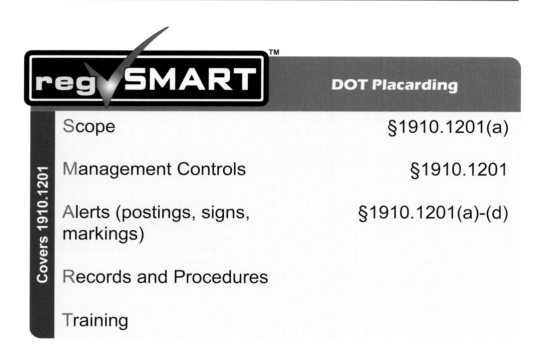

reg✓SMART™	DOT Placarding
Scope	§1910.1201(a)
Management Controls	§1910.1201
Alerts (postings, signs, markings)	§1910.1201(a)-(d)
Records and Procedures	
Training	

Covers 1910.1201

§1910.1201(a)

§1910.1201(b), (c)

§1910.1201(d)

DOT Markings, Placards, and Labels

Retain DOT markings until the container is cleaned of residue and purged of vapors to remove any potential hazards.

EPA requires containers to be triple-rinsed to remove all hazardous characteristics from the container.

Any employer who receives a shipment required to be placarded in accordance with the hazardous materials regulations must retain those placards until the hazardous materials are sufficiently removed to prevent any potential hazards.

Markings, placards, and labels must be readily visible.

For non-bulk packages that will not be reshipped, the DOT label can be removed if an OSHA-compliant label is affixed in accordance with the Hazard Communication Standard (29 CFR § 1910.1200).

© MCMXCVII - MMXIII by www.mancomm.com

Module Thirty-One

Hazard Communication, Part 2

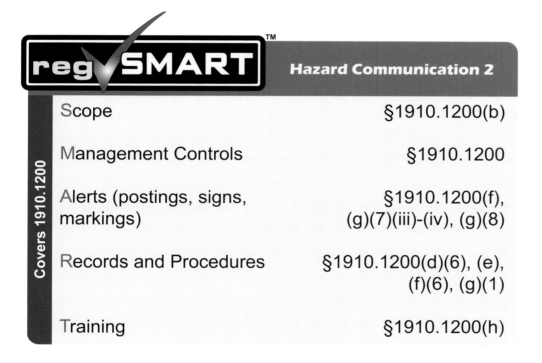

reg✓SMART™

Hazard Communication 2	
Scope	§1910.1200(b)
Management Controls	§1910.1200
Alerts (postings, signs, markings)	§1910.1200(f), (g)(7)(iii)-(iv), (g)(8)
Records and Procedures	§1910.1200(d)(6), (e), (f)(6), (g)(1)
Training	§1910.1200(h)

Covers 1910.1200

§1910.1200

Hazard Communication

HazCom is also known as "Right to Know."

Hazard communication is a continuing program, and compliance with the Hazard Communication Standard is NOT A ONE-SHOT DEAL.

The hazard communication standard is based on the three complementary parts of a comprehensive Hazard Communication Program:

> labels that provide a brief, but immediate and conspicuous, summary of hazard information at the site where the chemical is used

> safety data sheets (SDSs) that provide detailed technical information and serve as a reference source

> training that is designed to ensure that employees understand the chemical hazards in their workplace and are aware of protective measures to follow

The information required by the Hazard Communication Standard:

> reduces the incidence of chemical-related illnesses and injuries by enabling employers and employees to implement protective measures in the workplace;

> enables employers to select less hazardous chemical alternatives and ensure that appropriate engineering controls, work practices, and personal protective equipment (PPE) are in place;

> improves understanding of chemical hazards by supervisory personnel, resulting in safer handling of hazardous substances and proper storage and housekeeping measures;

> allows employees to fully participate in the protective measures instituted in their workplaces because they have been provided with information and training on chemical hazards;

> enables employees to become knowledgeable and take the steps required to work safely with chemicals and determine what actions are necessary if an emergency occurs;

> helps employees recognize signs and symptoms of chronic disease and seek early treatment;

> enables health and safety professionals to provide better services to exposed employees; and

> enhances medical surveillance, exposure monitoring, and other services by the ready availability of health and safety information.

© MCMXCVII - MMXIII by www.mancomm.com

§1910.1200(e)

OSHA inspectors will also be asking the following questions in assessing the adequacy of the program:

> Does a list of the hazardous chemicals exist in each work area or at a central location?

> Are methods the employer will use to inform employees of the hazards of non-routine tasks outlined?

> Are employees informed of the hazards associated with chemicals contained in unlabeled pipes in their work areas?

> On multi-employer worksites, has the employer provided other employers with information about labeling systems and precautionary measures where the other employers have employees exposed to the initial employer's chemicals?

> Is the written program made available to employees and their designated representatives?

If your program adequately addresses the means of communicating information to employees in your workplace and provides answers to the basic questions outlined above, it will be found to be in compliance with the rule.

HazCom Program

Elements of a HazCom Program include the following:

> Identify employee responsible for program maintenance.

> Develop a list of hazardous substances.

> Develop SDS procedures.

> Develop labeling procedures.

> Meet employee training requirements.

> Develop procedures to inform employees of the hazards of:

>> non-routine tasks, and

>> substances contained in unlabeled pipes.

§1910.1200(e)

§1910.1200(e)(1)(i)

> Develop multi-employer workplace procedures to inform contractors sharing the same work area of the hazardous substances to which their employees may be exposed:

>> Provide contractors access to SDSs.

>> Inform contractors of any precautionary measures to take.

>> Inform contractors of the company's labeling system.

> Establish procedures to keep the program current and evaluate its effectiveness.

Identify Responsible Personnel

It will be necessary to assign responsibility for both the initial and ongoing activities that must be undertaken to comply with the rule. **Remember:**

> Early identification of the responsible employees and involvement of them in the development of your plan of action will result in a more effective program design.

> Evaluation of the effectiveness of your program will also be enhanced by involvement of affected employees.

Develop a List of Hazardous Chemicals

The standard requires a list of hazardous chemicals in the workplace as part of the written hazard communication program. **Remember:**

> The best way to prepare a comprehensive list is to survey the workplace.

> Purchasing records may also help. Employers should establish procedures to ensure that in the future, purchasing procedures result in SDSs being received before a hazardous chemical is used in the workplace.

> Take a broad perspective when doing the survey. "Chemicals" are not just liquids in containers, but also liquids, solids, gases, vapors, fumes, and mists whether they are "contained" or not.

> Remember that the hazardous nature of the chemical and the potential for exposure are the factors that determine whether a chemical is covered. If a chemical is not hazardous, it is not covered by the HazCom standard. If there is no potential for exposure (e.g., the chemical is inextricably bound and cannot be released), then the chemical is not covered.

© MCMXCVII - MMXIII by www.mancomm.com

> Look around. Identify chemicals in containers, including pipes, but also think about chemicals generated in the work operations (welding fumes, dusts, exhaust fumes, etc.).

> Read labels provided by suppliers for hazard information and make a list of all chemicals in the workplace that are potentially hazardous, making sure to determine if any of the items can be eliminated because they are exempted materials (e.g., food, drugs, or cosmetics for employee consumption, etc.).

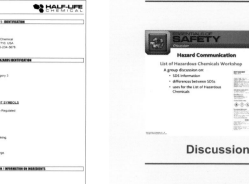

Discussion

List of Hazardous Chemicals Workshop

Handout: List of Hazardous Chemicals worksheet

The group will now discuss:

> SDS information

> differences between SDSs

> uses for the List of Hazardous Chemicals

Develop SDS Procedures

Chemical manufacturers and importers are required to obtain or develop a safety data sheet for each hazardous chemical they produce or import.

Employers must have an SDS for each hazardous chemical that they use.

The role of SDSs is to provide detailed information on each hazardous chemical, including:

> its potential hazardous effects

> its physical and chemical characteristics

> recommendations for appropriate protective measures

§1910.1200(g)

SDSs must be readily accessible to employees when they are in their work areas during their workshifts. As long as employees can get the information when they need it, any approach may be used:

> Some employers keep the SDSs in a binder in a central location.

> Others computerize the information and provide access through terminals.

To ensure that there is a current SDS for each hazardous chemical in the workplace as required, and that employee access is provided, an OSHA inspector will look for the following types of information in the written HazCom program:

> designation of person(s) responsible for obtaining and maintaining SDSs

> how SDSs are to be maintained in the workplace (e.g., notebooks in the work areas, computer with terminal access, etc.)

> how employees can obtain access to SDSs when they are in their work areas during the work shift

> procedures to follow when the SDS is not received at the time of the first shipment

> procedures to update the SDS when new and significant health information is found (mainly for chemical producers, but employers are also required to update their workplace labeling)

> description of alternatives to actual SDSs in the workplace, if used

The most important aspect of the written HazCom program in terms of SDSs is to ensure that someone is responsible for obtaining and maintaining SDSs for EVERY hazardous chemical in the workplace.

© MCMXCVII - MMXIII by www.mancomm.com

HazCom - SDS Workshop

Use the sample SDSs in the Student Workbook to fill in the information on the "SDS Workshop" worksheets.

Each workgroup will be assigned two chemicals to analyze on the worksheets. As a group, we will discuss:

> the hazards of the chemicals in question

> why the hazards of a chemical should be identified

> what the information on an SDS can be used for

> what the most important sections of an SDS are for workers using the chemical

Discussion

Develop Labeling Procedures

In-plant containers of hazardous chemicals must be labeled, tagged, or marked with:

> the identity of the material; and

> appropriate hazard warnings.

§1900.1200(f)(6)

For your labeling system:

> You can simply choose to use the labels provided by your suppliers on the containers.

> You can choose to create your own label containing the product identifier and words, pictures, symbols, or a combination that provide at least general information about the chemical's hazards.

>> This information, in conjunction with the other information that is immediately available to employees under the HazCom program, must provide employees with specific information regarding the physical and health hazards of the chemical.

The most important thing to remember is that this is a continuing duty. All in-plant containers of hazardous chemicals must always be labeled.

§1900.1200(f)(6)

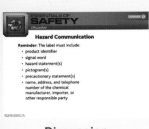

Discussion

§1910.1200(h)

§1910.1200(c)

Labeling Workshop

Each workgroup will use the sample SDSs for their assigned chemicals and use the "HazCom - Labeling Workshop" worksheet to develop labels that meet all OSHA requirements for labeling containers.

Each workgroup will chose a spokesperson to discuss:

> the importance of labeling containers using this method; and

> any specific areas of concern that may arise.

Reminder: The label must include:

> product identifier

> signal word

> hazard statement(s)

> pictogram(s)

> precautionary statement(s)

> name, address, and telephone number of the chemical manufacturer, importer, or other responsible party

Meet Employee Training Requirements

Each employee who may be "exposed" to hazardous chemicals when working must be provided information and trained prior to initial assignment to work with a hazardous chemical and whenever the hazard changes.

> "Exposure" or "exposed" is when an employee is subjected to a hazardous chemical in the course of employment through any route of entry (inhalation, ingestion, skin contact, or absorption).

> "Exposure" or "exposed" also includes potential exposure (accidental or possible).

© MCMXCVII - MMXIII by www.mancomm.com

OSHA Note

> A common problem encountered with HazCom training is the training is too generic. Instead of focusing on specific chemical hazards in the workplace, some employers make the mistake of only showing videos that deal with general situations.
> Another common error with training is no transfer of knowledge from the classroom training to practical application of working with hazardous chemicals on the job. This commonly occurs when the training is a "one-shot" deal with no further follow-up in the work areas while employees are working around and with hazardous chemicals.
> OSHA does not expect employees to recall all information provided in the training and be able to repeat it. However, employees must be aware of the hazards to which they are exposed, know how to obtain and use information on labels and SDSs, and to know and follow appropriate safe work practices.

§1910.1200(h)

Information and training may be designed to cover categories of hazards (e.g., flammability, carcinogenicity) or specific chemicals. However, chemical-specific information must ALWAYS be available through labels and safety data sheets.

> If there are only a few chemicals in the workplace, you may want to discuss each one individually.

> Where there are a large number of chemicals, or chemicals change frequently, you will probably want to train generally based on hazard classification (e.g., flammable solid, carcinogen, oral acute toxicity, etc.).

§1910.1200(h)

Information and training is a critical part of the hazard communication program.

› Information regarding hazards and protective measures are provided to workers through written labels and SDSs.

› Through effective information and training, workers will learn to:

» read and understand such information;

» determine how the information can be obtained and used in their own workplaces; and

» understand the risks of exposure to the chemicals in their workplaces as well as the ways to protect themselves.

In reviewing your written program with regard to information and training, the following items need to be considered:

› designation of person responsible for conducting training

› format of the program to be used (audiovisuals, classroom instruction, etc.)

› elements of the training program:

» the requirements of the HazCom Standard

» any operations in the work area where hazardous chemicals are present

» location and availability of the written HazCom program, list of hazardous chemicals, and safety data sheets

» how to detect the presence or release of a hazardous chemical

» physical, health, simply asphyxiation, combustible dust, pyrophoric gas hazards, and hazards not otherwise classified of the chemicals in the work area

» protective measures for chemical hazards

» details of the hazard communication program including labeling and location of SDSs

› procedure to train new employees at the time of their initial assignment to work with a hazardous chemical

› procedure to train employees when a new hazard is introduced into the workplace or the chemical (or hazard) changes

© MCMXCVII - MMXIII by www.mancomm.com

In general, the most important aspects of training under the Hazard Communication Standard are to ensure employees:

> are aware that they are exposed to hazardous chemicals;

> know how to read and use labels and safety data sheets; and

> follow the appropriate protective measures established by the employer.

OSHA compliance officers will be talking to employees to determine if they:

> have received training;

> know they are exposed to hazardous chemicals; and

> know where to obtain substance-specific information on labels and SDSs.

Training Documentation

The rule does not require employers to maintain records of employee training, but many employers choose to do so.

> This may help you monitor your own program to ensure that all employees are appropriately trained.

§1910.1200(h)

OSHA Field
Operations Manual

Editor's Insight

HazCom - Training Workshop

Use the "HazCom Training Workshop" worksheet from your Student Workbook.

> Each group will be assigned a chemical.

> Pick a spokesperson to train the entire group on your assigned chemical.

Refer to the "HazCom Sample Checklist" in your Student Workbook for compliance assistance.

§1910.1450

§1910.1450(a)(1), (b)

§1910.1450(a)(3)(ii), (b)

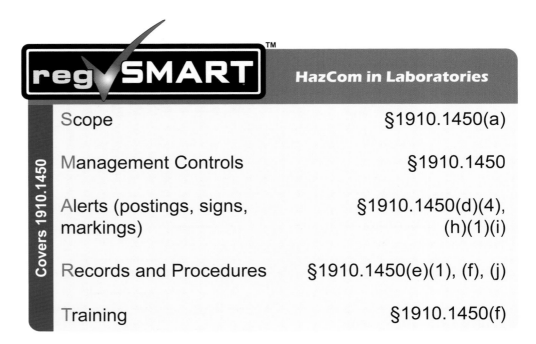

reg SMART™

HazCom in Laboratories

Covers 1910.1450

Scope	§1910.1450(a)
Management Controls	§1910.1450
Alerts (postings, signs, markings)	§1910.1450(d)(4), (h)(1)(i)
Records and Procedures	§1910.1450(e)(1), (f), (j)
Training	§1910.1450(f)

Laboratories

This section applies to all employers engaged in the laboratory use of hazardous chemicals.

"Laboratory use of hazardous chemicals" means the handling or use of such chemicals in which all of the following conditions are met:

> Chemical manipulations are carried out on a "laboratory scale."

>> "Laboratory scale" means the work must be done in containers that are designed to be easily and safely manipulated by one person. Production of commercial quantities is excluded.

> Multiple chemical procedures or chemicals are used.

> The procedures involved are not part of a production process, nor do they simulate a production process.

> Protective laboratory practices and equipment are available and in common use to minimize the potential for employee exposure to hazardous chemicals.

> Even if the chemical is undergoing "laboratory use," the Lab Standard does not apply if the procedure poses no risk of exposing employees to the chemical (e.g., use of dip-and-read test strips and commercial test kits where all reagents needed to conduct the test are included in the kit).

© MCMXCVII - MMXIII by www.mancomm.com

Chemical Hygiene Plan

The employer shall develop and carry out the provisions of a written chemical hygiene plan.

This plan shall include:

> standard operating procedures

> control measures to reduce employee exposure to hazardous chemicals, including engineering controls, the use of PPE, and hygiene practices

> a requirement that fume hoods and other protective equipment be functioning properly

> provisions for employee information and training

> circumstances under which a particular laboratory operation, procedure, or activity shall require prior approval from the employer

> provisions for medical consultation and medical examinations

> designation of personnel responsible for implementation of the chemical hygiene plan

> provisions for additional employee protection for work with particularly hazardous substances, including:

>> "select carcinogens"

>> reproductive toxins

>> substances having a high degree of acute toxicity

The employer shall review and evaluate the effectiveness of the chemical hygiene plan at least annually and update it as necessary.

§1910.1450(e)(1), (3), (4)

§1910.1450(f)(3)

§1910.1450(f)(4)

§1910.1450(i)

Employee Training

Employees shall be informed of:

> contents of this standard (which must be made available to employees)

> location and availability of the employer's chemical hygiene plan

> permissible exposure limits for OSHA-regulated substances (or recommended exposure limits for other hazardous chemicals where there is no applicable OSHA standard)

> signs and symptoms associated with exposures

> location and availability of known reference material, including, but not limited to, safety data sheets received from the chemical supplier

Employee training shall include:

> methods and observations that may be used to detect the presence or release of a hazardous chemical

> information on physical and health hazards of chemicals

> measures employees can take to protect themselves from these hazards

> the applicable details of the employer's written chemical hygiene plan

Respirators

Respirators shall be selected and used in accordance with the Respiratory Protection Standard, §1910.134.

Where the use of respirators is necessary to maintain exposure below permissible exposure limits, the employer shall provide, at no cost to the employee, the proper respiratory equipment.

© MCMXCVII - MMXIII by www.mancomm.com

Module Thirty-Two
Industrial Hygiene

Industrial Hygiene

Industrial hygiene is the art and science of anticipating, recognizing, evaluating, and controlling occupational and environmental health hazards in the workplace.

To detect the extend of worker exposure, industrial hygienists use:

› environmental monitoring; and

› analytical methods.

Industrial hygienists employ:

› Safety Order of Operations™

- Engineering controls
- Safe work practices
- Protective equipment

OSHA 3143, Informational
Booklet on Industrial Hygiene

OSHA relies on industrial hygienists to:

› evaluate jobs for potential health hazards; and

› develop and set mandatory occupational safety and health standards by:

» determining the extent of employee exposure to hazards, and

» deciding what is needed to control these hazards to protect workers.

More than 40 percent of the OSHA compliance officers who inspect America's workplaces are industrial hygienists. Industrial hygienists:

› play a major role in developing and issuing OSHA standards to protect workers from health hazards associated with toxic chemicals, biological hazards, and harmful physical agents;

› provide technical assistance and support to the agency's national and regional offices;

› assist in setting up field enforcement procedures and issue technical interpretations of OSHA regulations and standards; and

› analyze, identify, and measure workplace hazards or stresses that can cause sickness, impaired health, or significant discomfort in workers through chemical, physical, ergonomic, or biological exposures.

Two roles of OSHA's industrial hygienists:

1. Spot causal conditions.

2. Help eliminate or control causal conditions through appropriate measures.

Worksite Analysis

A worksite analysis is an essential first step that helps an industrial hygienist determine what jobs and workstations are the sources of potential problems.

› During the worksite analysis, the industrial hygienist measures and identifies exposures, problem tasks, and risks.

OSHA 3143, Informational Booklet on Industrial Hygiene

© MCMXCVII - MMXIII by www.mancomm.com

> The most effective worksite analyses include all jobs, operations, and work activities.

> The industrial hygienist inspects, researches, or analyzes how the particular chemicals or physical hazards at that worksite affect worker health.

> If a situation hazardous to health is discovered, the industrial hygienist recommends the appropriate corrective actions.

To be effective in recognizing and evaluating on the job hazards and recommending controls, industrial hygienists must be familiar with the hazards' characteristics such as:

> air contaminants

> chemical, biological, physical, and ergonomic hazards.

Air Contaminants

> These are commonly classified as either particulate or gas and vapor contaminants.

>> Common particulate contaminants include:

> dusts

> fumes

> mists

> aerosols

> fibers

Chemical Hazards

> Harmful chemical compounds in the form of solids, liquids, gases, mists, dusts, fumes, and vapors exert toxic effects after:

>> inhalation (breathing);

>> absorption (through direct contact with the skin); or

>> ingestion (eating or drinking).

OSHA 3143, Informational Booklet on Industrial Hygiene

OSHA 3143, Informational
Booklet on Industrial Hygiene

Biological Hazards

› These can cause acute and chronic infections by entering the body either directly or through breaks in the skin.

» These hazards include:

› bacteria

› viruses

› fungi

› other living organisms

› Occupations at risk for biological hazards include:

» industries that deal with plants or animals or their products

» industries with food and food processing

» health care

Physical Hazards

› These include:

» excessive levels of ionizing and non-ionizing electromagnetic radiation

» noise

» vibration

» illumination

» temperature

› **Radiation:**

» Distance is a valuable tool in controlling exposure to both ionizing and non-ionizing radiation.

» The shorter the time of exposure, the smaller the radiation danger.

» Shielding is a way to protect against radiation.

› The greater the protective mass between a radioactive source and the worker, the lower the radiation exposure.

© MCMXCVII - MMXIII by www.mancomm.com

> **Noise:**

>> Another significant physical hazard which can be controlled by various measures.

> Safety Order of Operations™

- Engineering controls
- Safe work practices
- Protective equipment

Order of Operations™

™

Safety STOP

Safety Tip

Check with the loss control specialist of your worker's compensation insurance company when monitoring is needed in the workplace; they can oftentimes help you with noise monitoring and air-quality monitoring. If not, they may be able to recommend an industrial hygienist who can monitor your workplace.

Ergonomic Hazards

> The science of ergonomics studies and evaluates a full range of tasks, including but not limited to:

>> lifting

>> holding

>> pushing

>> walking

>> reaching

Heat Stress

> **Causes:**

>> Heat stress can be caused by high air temperatures, radiant heat sources, high humidity, direct physical contact with hot objects, or strenuous physical activities. There are varying degrees of heat disorders and health effects.

OSHA 3143, Informational Booklet on Industrial Hygiene

Editor's Insight

Editor's Insight

> **Engineering Controls:**

>> Ventilation, air cooling, fans, shielding, and insulation are the five major types of engineering controls used to reduce heat stress in hot work environments.

> **Safe Work Practices:**

>> Another way to reduce heat stress is to allow workers to take regular rest breaks in a cooler place.

>> Water should be made available to workers to encourage them to drink small amounts frequently, e.g., one cup every 20 minutes.

> **Refer to the NIOSH Heat Stress Facts" handout in your Student Workbook.**

Conclusion

> Industrial hygiene encompasses a broad spectrum of the working environment.

> By recognizing and applying the principles of industrial hygiene to the work environment, America's workplaces will become safer.

© MCMXCVII - MMXIII by www.mancomm.com

Module Thirty-Three
Open Forum

A. Do you have workplace issues?

B. Think about these questions for the open forum:

1. How can we convince employees to become involved in safety?

2. How can we attain management's commitment toward safety?

3. How do we get supervisors to be responsible for safety?

4. How can we change employee or management behavior toward safety?

5. How well do safety incentive programs work?

6. How can we effectively discipline our employees?

7. What effect does reverse psychology have on employees or management in order to getting them more involved or committed to safety?

8. How can we effectively train our employees?

Discussion

Notes

© MCMXCVII - MMXIII by www.mancomm.com

Module Thirty-Four

Hazardous Materials

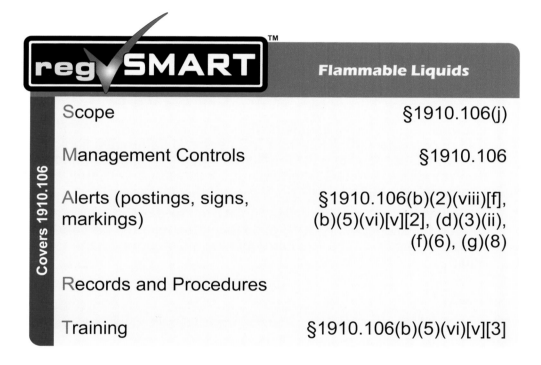

reg✓SMART™	Flammable Liquids
Scope	§1910.106(j)
Management Controls	§1910.106
Alerts (postings, signs, markings)	§1910.106(b)(2)(viii)[f], (b)(5)(vi)[v][2], (d)(3)(ii), (f)(6), (g)(8)
Records and Procedures	
Training	§1910.106(b)(5)(vi)[v][3]

Covers 1910.106

§1910.106(a)(14)

§1910.106(a)(19)

Flammable Liquid Definitions

Flashpoint:

> Temperature at which a liquid gives off vapor in sufficient concentration to form an ignitable mixture with air near the surface of the liquid.

Flammable Liquid:

> Any liquid having a flashpoint at or below 199.4°F. Flammable liquids are divided into four categories:

>> **Category 1:** Includes liquids having flashpoints below 73.4°F and having a boiling point at or below 95°F.

>> **Category 2:** Includes liquids having flashpoints below 73.4°F and having a boiling point above 95°F.

>> **Category 3:** Includes liquids having flashpoints at or above 73.4°F and at or below 140°F. When a Category 3 liquid with a flashpoint at or above 100°F is heated for use to within 30°F of its flashpoint, it must be handled in accordance with the requirements for a Category 3 liquid with a flashpoint below 100°F.

>> **Category 4:** Includes liquids having flashpoints above 140°F and at or below 199.4°F. When a Category 4 flammable liquid is heated for use to within 30°F of its flashpoint, it must be handled in accordance with the requirements for a Category 3 liquid with a flashpoint at or above 100°F.

>> **Note:** When a liquid with a flashpoint greater than 199.4°F is heated for use to within 30°F of its flashpoint, it must be handled in accordance with the requirements for a Category 4 flammable liquid.

SDS Information

Gasoline chemical characteristics

> Flashpoint (-45°F)

> Boiling point (85°F to 437°F)

Since the boiling point has a temperature range, instead of a specific temperature, the worst case scenario that must be used is 85°F. Therefore, gasoline is a Category 1 flammable liquid.

© MCMXCVII - MMXIII by www.mancomm.com

Container Storage

The following sections apply to container storage requirements for flammable liquids in containers with a capacity of 60 gallons or less and portable tanks not exceeding a capacity of 660 gallons.

OSHA Note – §1910.106 (a)(29)

"Safety can" shall mean an approved container of not more than 5 gallons capacity having a spring-closing lid and spout cover, and so designed that it will safely relieve internal pressure when subjected to fire exposure.

Table H-12 — Maximum Allowable Size of Containers and Portable Tanks for Flammable Liquids

Container Type	Category 1	Category 2	Category 3	Category 4
Glass or approved plastic	1 pt	1 qt	1 gal	1 gal
Metal (other than DOT drums)	1 gal	5 gal	5 gal	5 gal
Safety cans	2 gal	5 gal	5 gal	5 gal
Metal drums (DOT specifications)	60 gal	60 gal	60 gal	60 gal
Approved portable tanks	660 gal	660 gal	660 gal	660 gal

Note: Container exemptions: (a) Medicines, beverages, foodstuffs, cosmetics, and other common consumer items, when packaged according to commonly accepted practices, shall be exempt from the requirements of §1910.106(d)(2)(i) and (ii).

Office Occupancies

Storage of flammable liquids is prohibited except that which is required for maintenance and operation of buildings and equipment. Keep flammable liquids in:

> safety cans;

> closed metal containers stored inside a storage cabinet; or

> inside a storage room. (The door of this room cannot open into an area of the building used by the public.)

§1910.106(d)(1)(i)

§1910.106(d)(2)(ii)
Table H-12

§1910.106(d)(5)(iii)

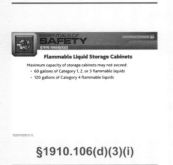

§1910.106(d)(3)(i)

§1910.106(d)(3)(ii)

§1910.106(d)(3)(ii)[a]

§1910.106(d)(3)(ii)[b]

§1910.106(d)(3)(ii)

Flammable Liquid Storage Cabinets

Maximum capacity of storage cabinets may not exceed:

> 60 gallons of Category 1, 2, or 3 flammable liquids

> 120 gallons of Category 4 flammable liquids

Storage cabinets must limit the internal temperature to not more than 325°F when subjected to a 10-minute fire test.

> All joints and seams must remain tight and the door securely closed during the fire test.

Metal cabinets must:

> be made of at least No. 18 gage sheet iron and double-walled with 1 ½ inches of air space;

> have joints that are riveted, welded, or made tight by some equally effective means;

> have a three-point lock; and

> have a door sill that is raised at least 2 inches above the bottom of the cabinet.

Wooden cabinets must:

> be made of an approved grade of plywood at least 1 inch thick that does not break down or delaminate under fire conditions;

> have joints that are rabbeted and fastened in two directions with flathead woodscrews;

> have a rabbeted overlap of at least 1 inch when more than one door is used; and

> have hinges that are mounted so as not to lose their holding capacity due to loosening or burning out of the screws when subjected to the fire test.

Cabinets must be labeled:

FLAMMABLE KEEP FIRE AWAY

© MCMXCVII - MMXIII by www.mancomm.com

NFPA 30, Chapter 4-3.4 & NFPA 99, Chapter 10-7.2.3

Flammable liquid storage cabinets are not required to be vented except for the control of materials with a bad odor. Seal vent openings with the bungs supplied with the cabinet or with bungs specified by the manufacturer of the cabinet. If vented, vent cabinet from the bottom with make-up air supplied to the top. Vent the cabinet outdoors to an approved location or through a flame arrester to a fume hood exhaust system. Construction of the venting duct should be equal to the rating of the cabinet.

Inside Storage Rooms

Construction

Inside storage rooms shall be constructed to meet the required fire-resistive rating for their use.

> 1-hour or 2-hour fire-resistance rating per §1910.106, Table H-13.
> Where an automatic sprinkler system is provided, the system shall be designed and installed in an acceptable manner.

Openings to other rooms or buildings shall be provided with one of the following:

> non-combustible, liquid-tight raised sills;
> ramps at least 4 inches in height;
> floor in a storage room floor that is at least 4 inches below surrounding floor;
> openings with approved self-closing fire doors; or
> liquid-tight room where walls join floor

Note: A permissible alternate to a sill or ramp is an open-grated trench inside of the room that drains to a safe location

Where other portions of building or other property are exposed, fire windows must be installed; or

Shelving, racks, and similar installations may be made of wood that is at least 1 inch nominal thickness.

§1910.106(d)(4)(i)

§1910.106(d)(4)(ii)

§1910.106(d)(4)(iii)

§1910.106(d)(4)(iv)

Rating and Capacity

Storage in inside rooms shall comply with:

Table H-13 — Storage in Inside Rooms			
Fire protection provided[a]	Fire resistance	Maximum size	Total allowable quantities (gals./sq. ft./floor area)
Yes	2 hours	500 sq. ft.	10
No	2 hours	500 sq. ft.	4[b]
Yes	1 hour	150 sq. ft.	5[c]
No	1 hour	150 sq. ft.	2

a. Fire protection must be sprinkler, water spray, carbon dioxide, or other system.

b. According to OSHA's Small Business Training guide for Flammable and Combustible Liquids, this number should be 4. See the Links page on www.oshacfr.com for more details. The NFPA 30 "Flammable and Combustible Liquids Code" also states that number should be 4 gal./sq.ft. in a 500 sq.ft. room with No Fire Protection

c. According to OSHA's Small Business Training guide for Flammable and Combustible Liquids, this number should be 5. See the Links page on www.oshacfr.com for more details. The NFPA 30 "Flammable and Combustible Liquids Code" also states that number should be 5 gal./sq.ft. in a 150 sq.ft. room with Fire Protection

Wiring

Electrical wiring and equipment located inside storage rooms used for any of the following must be approved under Subpart S of the OSHA regulations for Class I, Division 2 Hazardous Locations:

> Category 1 flammable liquids

> Category 2 flammable liquids

> Category 3 flammable liquids with a flashpoint below 100°F

Electrical wiring and equipment located inside storage rooms used for Category 3 flammable liquids with a flashpoint at or above 100°F and/or Category 4 flammable liquids must be approved for general use.

Ventilation

Every inside storage room must have either a gravity or a mechanical exhaust ventilation system. The system must:

> provide for a complete change of air within the room at least 6 times per hour;

© MCMXCVII - MMXIII by www.mancomm.com

> be controlled by a switch located outside of the door that also controls the lights, if a mechanical exhaust system is used; and

>> **Note:** The switch must have a pilot light installed adjacent to it if Category 1 or 2 flammable liquids or Category 3 flammable liquids with a flashpoint below 100°F are dispensed within the room.

> have the fresh air intake and exhaust outlet on the exterior of the building, if gravity ventilation is used.

§1910.106(d)(4)(iv)

Storage

Do the following when storing flammable liquids in inside storage rooms:

> Ensure that there is one clear aisle at least 3 feet wide.

> Do not stack containers over 30-gallons in capacity on top of each other.

> Dispense flammable or combustible liquids by an approved pump or self-closing faucet only.

§1910.106(d)(4)(v)

OSHA Letter of Interpretation — 04/23/96: Sadler

According to the definitions of "storage" and "container," time is not a relevant factor when considering how long a liquid must be in a container to be considered stored.

> As long as the liquid is contained in a container that is an integral component of the equipment, it can be stored for any length of time, and it would not be considered in "storage."

> Otherwise, if the liquid is kept in a storage container that is not an integral part of machinery, that container is considered in "storage" at all times. container to be considered stored.

§1910.106(d)(5)(i)

Egress

Flammable or combustible liquids cannot be stored where they limit the use of exits, stairways, or areas normally used for the safe egress of personnel.

Warehouse Storage

If the warehouse or storage building is located 50 feet or less from a building or line of adjoining property that may be built on, the exposing wall shall be a blank wall having a fire-resistance rating of at least 2 hours.

Although the total quantity of liquids that may be stored within a warehouse is not restricted, the arrangement of the storage must comply with §1910.106(d)(5)(vi), Table H-14 or H-15

§1910.106(d)(5)(vi)[a], [b]

Warehouse Storage

Ensure portable tanks stored over one tier high:
· are designed to nest securely; and
· have adequate powered industrial trucks available to handle tanks safely.

§1910.106(d)(5)(vi)[d]

Warehouse Storage

Ensure no pile shall be closer than:
· 3 feet from the nearest beam, chord, girder, or other obstruction; or
· 3 feet below sprinkler deflectors or to other fire protection systems.

Aisles at least 3 feet wide shall be provided where necessary for reasons of access to:
· doors
· windows
· standpipe connections

§1910.106(d)(5)(vi)[e], [f]

Warehouse Storage

If the warehouse or storage building is located 50 feet or less from a building or line of adjoining property that may be built on, the exposing wall shall be a blank wall having a fire-resistance rating of at least 2 hours.

Although the total quantity of liquids that may be stored within a warehouse is not restricted, the arrangement of the storage must comply with §1910.106(d)(5)(vi), Table H-14 or H-15.

Ensure portable tanks stored over one tier high:

> are designed to nest securely; and

> have adequate powered industrial trucks available to handle tanks safely.

Ensure no pile shall be closer than:

> 3 feet from the nearest beam, chord, girder, or other obstruction; or

> 3 feet below sprinkler deflectors or other fire protection systems.

Aisles at least 3 feet wide shall be provided where necessary for reasons of access to:

> doors

> windows

> standpipe connections

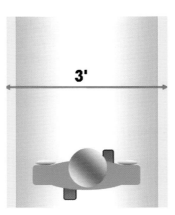

© MCMXCVII - MMXIII by www.mancomm.com

Outside Storage

Storage outside buildings must be in accordance with the following:

Table H-16 — Outdoor Container Storage				
1-Category	2-Maximum per pile	3-Distance between piles	4-Distance to property line that can be built upon	5-Distance to street, alley, public way
	gallons	feet	feet	feet
1	1,100	5	20	10
2	2,200	5	20	10
3 (FP<100F)	4,400	5	20	10
3 (FP≥100F)	8,800	5	10	5
4	22,000	5	10	5

NOTE 1: When 2 or more categories of materials are stored in a single pile, the maximum gallonage in that pile shall be the smallest of the 2 or more separate gallonages.

NOTE 2: Within 200 ft. of each container, there shall be a 12 ft. wide access way to permit approach of fire control apparatus.

NOTE 3: The distances listed apply to properties that have protection for exposures as defined. If there are exposures, and such protection for exposures does not exist, the distances in column 4 shall be doubled.

NOTE 4: When total quantity stored does not exceed 50 percent of maximum per pile, the distances in columns 4 and 5 may be reduced 50 percent, but not less than 3 ft.

NOTE 5: FP means Flashpoint.

Table H-17 — Outdoor Portable Tank Storage				
1-Category	2-Maximum per pile	3-Distance between piles	4-Distance to property line that can be built upon	5-Distance to street, alley, public way
	gallons	feet	feet	feet
1	2,200	5	20	10
2	4,400	5	20	10
3 (FP<100F)	8,800	5	20	10
3 (FP≥100F)	17,600	5	10	5
4	44,000	5	10	5

NOTE 1: When 2 or more categories of materials are stored in a single pile, the maximum gallonage in that pile shall be the smallest of the 2 or more separate gallonages.

NOTE 2: Within 200 ft. of each portable tank, there shall be a 12 ft. wide access way to permit approach of fire control apparatus.

NOTE 3: The distances listed apply to properties that have protection for exposures as defined. If there are exposures, and such protection for exposures does not exist, the distances in column 4 shall be doubled.

NOTE 4: When total quantity stored does not exceed 50 percent of maximum per pile, the distances in columns 4 and 5 may be reduced 50 percent, but not less than 3 ft.

NOTE 5: FP means Flashpoint.

§1910.106(d)(6)(i)

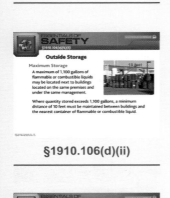

§1910.106(d)(ii)

§1910.106(d)(iii)

Maximum Storage

A maximum of 1,100 gallons of flammable or combustible liquids may be located next to buildings located on the same premises and under the same management.

Where quantity stored exceeds 1,100 gallons, a minimum distance of 10 feet must be maintained between buildings and the nearest container of flammable or combustible liquid.

Spill Containment

Grade the storage area in a manner to divert possible spills away from buildings or other exposures, or surround the storage area with a curb at least six inches high.

> Make certain when curbs are used, provisions are made for draining accumulations of ground or rain water or spills of flammable or combustible liquids. Don't forget about the EPA's storm water permit.

> Drains must end at a safe location and be accessible to operations during fire conditions.

Security

Make certain the storage area is secure by:

> protecting the area against tampering or trespassers; and

> keeping the area free of weeds, debris, and other combustible material not necessary to the storage

§1910.106(d)(6)(iv)

© MCMXCVII - MMXIII by www.mancomm.com

Fire Control

Suitable fire control, such as portable fire extinguishers, shall be available at locations where flammable or combustible liquids are stored.

› At least one portable fire extinguisher rated not less than 12-B must be located outside of, but not more than 10 feet from, the door opening into any room used for storage.

› At least one portable fire extinguisher rated not less than 12-B must be located not less than 10 feet, nor more than 25 feet, from any Category 1, 2, or 3 flammable liquid storage area located outside of a storage room but inside a building.

Open flames and smoking shall not be permitted in flammable or combustible liquid storage areas.

Materials that will react with water shall not be stored in the same room with flammable or combustible liquids.

§1910.106(d)(7), (7)(i)

§1910.106(d)(7)(iii), (iv)

§1910.119

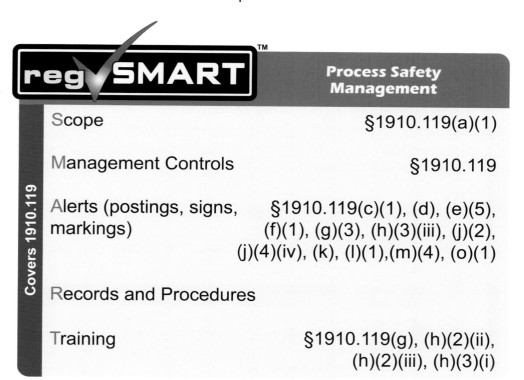

Covers 1910.119

reg✔SMART™	Process Safety Management
Scope	§1910.119(a)(1)
Management Controls	§1910.119
Alerts (postings, signs, markings)	§1910.119(c)(1), (d), (e)(5), (f)(1), (g)(3), (h)(3)(iii), (j)(2), (j)(4)(iv), (k), (l)(1),(m)(4), (o)(1)
Records and Procedures	
Training	§1910.119(g), (h)(2)(ii), (h)(2)(iii), (h)(3)(i)

§1910.119

§1910.119(a)(1)

§1910.119(a)(1)(i)[A]

§1910.119(a)(1)(ii)[B], (a)(2)

Process Safety Management

The Process Safety Management of Highly Hazardous Chemicals Standard is intended to prevent or minimize the consequences of catastrophic releases of toxic, reactive, flammable, or explosive chemicals that could result in toxic, fire, or explosion hazards.

Process safety managements applies to the following:

> a process that involves a chemical at or above the OSHA-specified threshold quantity

> a process that involves a flammable liquid or gas onsite in one location in a quantity of 10,000 pounds or more

Process safety management does NOT apply to:

> hydrocarbon fuels (such as gasoline and propane) used solely as a fuel, so long as the fuel is not part of a process containing another highly hazardous chemical covered by the standard; or

>> Note, however, that other hazardous materials standards such as §1910.106 and §1910.110 may apply.

> flammable liquids stored in atmospheric tanks, so long as they are kept below their normal boiling point without benefit of chilling or refrigeration;

> retail facilities;

> oil or gas well drilling or servicing operations; or

> normally unoccupied remote facilities.

Letter of Interpretation — 2/01/02: Olesen

More than 10,000 lbs. of flammable liquids stored in 55 gallon drums would be considered exempt as storage in atmospheric tanks, unless the drums are near a process covered by process safety management.

© MCMXCVII - MMXIII by www.mancomm.com

When highly hazardous chemicals exist in your warehouse or process, an employer may elect to separate containers of highly hazardous chemicals so a threshold quantity does not exist.

> In this case, the piles of containers would be separated far enough from each other that a single event could not result in a threshold quantity release.

OSHA Letter of Interpretation

Process safety management involves the following:

> employee participation

> process safety information

> process hazard analysis

> operating procedures

> training

> pre-startup safety review

> mechanical integrity

> procedures for process changes

> incident investigation

> emergency planning and response

> compliance audits by the employer

§1910.119(c)-(g), (i), (l)-(o)

Operating Procedures

Written operating procedures that provide clear instructions for safely conducting activities involved in each covered process are required. At a minimum, these procedures must address:

> steps for each operating phase:

>> initial startup

>> normal operations

>> temporary operations

>> emergency shutdown

>> emergency operations

>> normal shutdown

>> startup following a turnaround or after an emergency shutdown

§1910.119(f)(1)(i)

§1910.119(f)(1)(ii)-(iv)

§1910.119(f)(2), (3)

§1910.119(g)

> operating limits:
>> consequences of deviation
>> steps required to correct or avoid deviation
> safety and health considerations:
>> properties of, and hazards presented by, the chemicals used
>> necessary precautions
>> control measures to be taken if exposure occurs
>> quality control for raw materials and control of hazardous chemical inventory levels
>> any special or unique hazards
> safety systems and their functions

Operating procedures must be readily accessible to employees who work in or maintain a process. Procedures must be reviewed as often as necessary to assure they reflect current operating practice. Employers must certify annually that the operating procedures are current and accurate.

Training for Process Safety Management

Training requirements include:
> initial training for employees involved in operating a process
> retraining at least every 3 years
> document the training
>> identity of employee
>> date of training
>> proof that employee understood the training

An employer's training program would also include:
> HazCom training
> emergency action plan training for minor releases
> emergency response training for significant releases

© MCMXCVII - MMXIII by www.mancomm.com

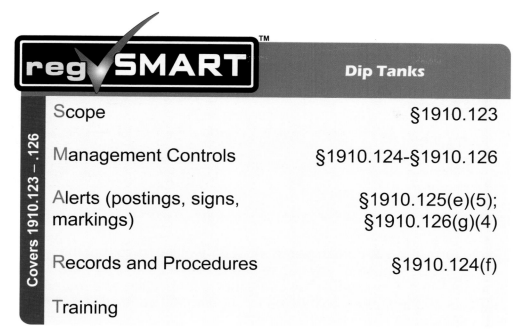

reg✓SMART™	Dip Tanks	
Scope		§1910.123
Management Controls		§1910.124-§1910.126
Alerts (postings, signs, markings)		§1910.125(e)(5); §1910.126(g)(4)
Records and Procedures		§1910.124(f)
Training		

Covers 1910.123 – .126

§1910.123(d)

§1910.123(a)

Dip Tanks

A dip tank is a container that holds a liquid other than water and that is used for dipping or coating.

> An object may be immersed (or partially immersed) in a dip tank, or it may be suspended in a vapor coming from the tank.

OSHA considers parts cleaners (sink-on-drum) to be a dip tank.

Dip tank requirements apply when using liquid in the tank or its vapor to:

> clean an object;

> coat an object;

> alter the surface of an object;

> change the character of an object; or

> drain and dry an object you have dipped or coated.

§1910.123(b)

§1910.123(b)(1), (3)

§1910.124(g)

Examples of dip tank operations include:

> paint dipping
> electroplating
> pickling
> quenching
> tanning
> degreasing

> cleaning
> roll coating
> flow coating
> curtain coating
> stripping

Ventilation

The dip tank and surrounding area must be ventilated so that the airborne concentration of any substance is below 25% of its lower flammable limit. Employers may use either a tank cover or a material that floats on the surface to replace or supplement ventilation as long as the standard's requirements are met.

Personal Hygiene

When your employees work with liquids that may burn, irritate, or otherwise harm their skin, employers must provide:

> locker space or other storage space to prevent contamination of the employee's street clothes;

> an emergency shower and eyewash station close to the dipping or coating operation; and

   Note: In place of this equipment, you may use a water hose that is:

   » at least 4 feet long,

   » at least 3/4 of an inch thick,

   » with a quick-opening valve, and

   » carrying a pressure of 25 pounds per square inch or less.

> at least one basin with a hot-water faucet for every 10 employees who work with such liquids.

© MCMXCVII - MMXIII by www.mancomm.com

Module Thirty-Five

Recordkeeping, Part 2

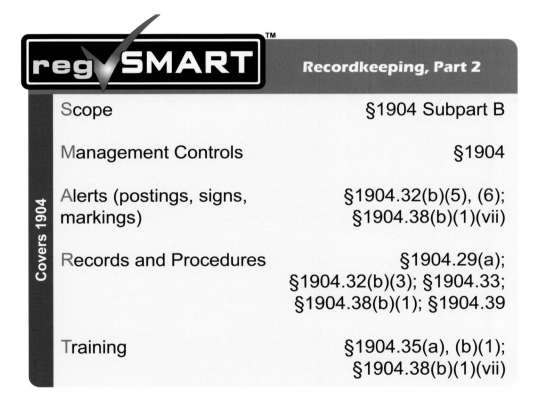

reg✔SMART™	Recordkeeping, Part 2
Scope	§1904 Subpart B
Management Controls	§1904
Alerts (postings, signs, markings)	§1904.32(b)(5), (6); §1904.38(b)(1)(vii)
Records and Procedures	§1904.29(a); §1904.32(b)(3); §1904.33; §1904.38(b)(1); §1904.39
Training	§1904.35(a), (b)(1); §1904.38(b)(1)(vii)

Covers 1904

Discussion

300 Log

Discussion

Recordkeeping Workshop

Handout: OSHA 301 Form (found with Module 7 handouts)

Using the Quick Start Guide™ each person will determine if the following incident is recordable and justify your decision with regulations. If it is recordable, enter the case onto an OSHA 301 Form.

Incident:

Zach Hayden spent his holiday season celebrating his 40th birthday. On December 30th, he moved into a new house at 104 State Street in Saratoga, Wyoming. Just as Zach was punching in at 7:00 on the morning of January 2, he was thinking about how long he'd been with SLE Corp. and determined it'll be 14 years in 3 days. Zach was the only receiving clerk on the loading dock that day. It was a little after 8:00 when at he cut his left hand with a box cutter while opening a box. He was sent to the emergency room at the hospital, and Dr. Howard used 4 stitches to close the wound. Zach took the rest of the day off, but he returned to work the next day.

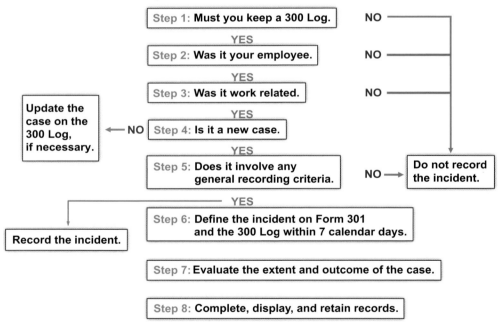

Quick Start Guide

Step 1: **Must you keep a 300 Log.** — NO

YES

Step 2: **Was it your employee.** — NO

YES

Step 3: **Was it work related.** — NO

YES

Update the case on the 300 Log, if necessary. ← NO Step 4: **Is it a new case.**

YES

Step 5: **Does it involve any general recording criteria.** — NO → **Do not record the incident.**

YES

Record the incident.

Step 6: **Define the incident on Form 301 and the 300 Log within 7 calendar days.**

Step 7: **Evaluate the extent and outcome of the case.**

Step 8: **Complete, display, and retain records.**

© MCMXCVII - MMXIII by www.mancomm.com

Each person will now use the OSHA 300 Log, found in your Student Workbook, for the cases on the following page.

> Is the injury or illness recordable?

> Are there any days away from work?

> Do we need to report this to OSHA?

Cases:

At SLE Corp., it has started as the year of accidents. The following is a list of injuries and illnesses. Each person will now enter the recordable injuries and illnesses on the OSHA 300 Log in your Student Workbook. Don't forget to use the 8 Steps to Recordkeeping™.

Recordkeeping Workshop

Cases:
At SLE Corp., it has started as the year of accidents. The following is a list of injuries and illnesses.
- Jan. 14, Janie Sears, a machine operator, had a hearing test that showed a standard threshold shift in hearing of 15 decibels and measured 20 decibels above audiometric zero.
- Feb. 08, Mary Davis, a human resource manager, fainted, which the doctor says is due to the flu. She was off work for 2 days.

Recordkeeping Workshop
- Feb. 14, John Matlock, a maintenance worker, fell off the roof during building maintenance. He was hospitalized for 42 days for internal injuries and then died from complications.
- Feb. 29, Kelly Lock, a mechanical press operator, lost her right index finger in the press. She was off work for 2 weeks.
- Feb. 29, Mark Woods, also a press operator, tried to help Kelly with her injury, but blood splashed into his eyes.

> Jan. 14, Janie Sears, a machine operator, had a hearing test that showed a standard threshold shift in hearing of 15 decibels and measured 20 decibels above audiometric zero.

> Feb. 08, Mary Davis, a human resource manager, fainted, which the doctor says is due to the flu. She was off work for 2 days.

> Feb. 14, John Matlock, a maintenance worker, fell off the roof during building maintenance. He was hospitalized for 42 days for internal injuries and then died from complications.

> Feb. 29, Kelly Lock, a mechanical press operator, lost her right index finger in the press. She was off work for 2 weeks.

> Feb. 29, Mark Woods, also a press operator, tried to help Kelly with her injury, but blood splashed into his eyes.

Recordkeeping Workshop
- Mar. 18, Lisa Regis, a data entry person, slipped on a wet floor at work and hurt her back. She was off work for 7 months.
- Apr. 14, Carl Mulls, a machine operator, developed a skin rash on his right arm from contact with cleaning chemicals. The doctor prescribed a prescription ointment as treatment.

Discussion

> Mar. 18, Lisa Regis, a data entry person, slipped on a wet floor at work and hurt her back. She was off work for 7 months.

> Apr. 14, Carl Mulls, a machine operator, developed a skin rash on his right arm from contact with cleaning chemicals. The doctor prescribed a prescription ointment as treatment.

Safety STOP ™

OSHA Inspection Directive — CPL 02-00-135

Penalties

› 300 Log: When a penalty is appropriate, there will be an unadjusted penalty of $1,000 for each year the OSHA 300 Log was not properly kept.

› 301 Form: An unadjusted penalty of $1,000 for each OSHA 301 Form that was not filled out at all (up to a maximum of $7,000), and an unadjusted penalty of $1,000 for each OSHA 301 form that was not accurately completed (up to a maximum of $3,000).

› 300A Summary: An other-than-serious citation will normally be issued for each OSHA 300A form improperly posted, certified, or filled out; the unadjusted penalty for this violation is $1,000.

© MCMXCVII - MMXIII by www.mancomm.com

Module Thirty-Six
Ergonomics

Ergonomics and the General Duty Clause

Definition

Ergonomics is an applied science dealing with the design and arrangement of the things people use so that the people and things interact safely and efficiently.

Basically, this means that jobs should be designed with human needs and limitations in mind in order to avoid unnecessary injuries. Ergonomics is mostly concerned with musculoskeletal disorders (MSDs), which are discussed below.

OSHA enforces ergonomics under Section 5(a)(1) of the "Act" referred to as the General Duty Clause:

› The General Duty Clause requires employers to furnish a workplace free from recognized hazards that could cause death or serious injury to employees.

› Therefore, causes of repetitive motion injuries must be corrected.

» An effective means to identify ergonomic issues is through workplace analysis.

**Section 5(a)(1)
of the OSH Act**

OSHA National News Release

U.S. Department of Labor
OSHA, Office of Communications

National News Release   USDL 02-201
Date: Apr. 5, 2002
Contact: Sue Hensley (202) 693-4676
Bonnie Friedman (202) 693-1999

OSHA Announces Comprehensive Plan To Reduce Ergonomic Injuries
Targeted Guidelines and Tough Enforcement Two Key Elements

WASHINGTON - The Occupational Safety and Health Administration today unveiled a comprehensive plan designed to dramatically reduce ergonomic injuries through a combination of industry-targeted guidelines, tough enforcement measures, workplace outreach, advanced research, and dedicated efforts to protect Hispanic and other immigrant workers.

"Our goal is to help workers by reducing ergonomic injuries in the shortest possible time frame," said Labor Secretary Elaine L. Chao. "This plan is a major improvement over the rejected old rule because it will prevent ergonomics injuries before they occur and reach a much larger number of at-risk workers."

Guidelines

Occupational Safety and Health Administrator John Henshaw said his agency will immediately begin work on developing industry and task-specific guidelines to reduce and prevent ergonomic injuries, often called musculoskeletal disorders (MSDs), that occur in the workplace. OSHA expects to begin releasing guidelines ready for application in selected industries this year. OSHA will also encourage other businesses and industries to immediately develop additional guidelines of their own.

Enforcement

The Department's ergonomics enforcement plan will crack down on bad actors by coordinating inspections with a legal strategy designed for successful prosecution. The Department will place special emphasis on industries with the sorts of serious ergonomics problems that OSHA and DOL attorneys have successfully addressed in prior 5(a)(1) or General Duty clause cases, including the **Beverly Enterprises** and **Pepperidge Farm** cases. For the first time, OSHA will have an enforcement plan designed from the start to target prosecutable ergonomic violations. Also for the first time, inspections will be coordinated with a legal strategy developed by DOL attorneys that is based on prior successful ergonomics cases and is designed to maximize successful prosecutions. And, OSHA will have special ergonomics inspection teams that will, from the earliest stages, work closely with DOL attorneys and experts to successfully bring prosecutions under the General Duty clause.

Compliance Assistance

The new ergonomics plan also calls for compliance assistance tools to help workplaces reduce and prevent ergonomic injuries. OSHA will provide specialized training and information on guidelines and the implementation of successful ergonomics programs. It will also administer targeted training grants, develop compliance assistance tools, forge partnerships and create a recognition program to highlight successful ergonomics injury reduction efforts.

Hispanic Outreach

As part of the Department of Labor's cross-agency commitment to protecting immigrant workers, especially those with limited English proficiency, the new ergonomics plan includes a specialized focus to help Hispanic and other immigrant workers, many of whom work in industries with high ergonomic hazard rates.

Ergonomics Research

The plan also includes the announcement of a national advisory committee; part of their task will be to advise OSHA on research gaps. In concert with the National Institute for Occupational Safety and Health, OSHA will stimulate and encourage needed research in this area.

"Bureau of Labor Statistics' data show that musculoskeletal disorders are already on the decline. This plan is designed to accelerate that decline as quickly as possible," said OSHA Administrator John Henshaw. "Thousands of employers are already working to reduce ergonomic risks without government mandates. We want to work with them to continuously improve workplace safety and health. We will go after the bad actors who refuse to take care of their workers."

The new plan was announced barely a year after Republicans and Democrats in Congress rejected the previous Administration's rule, which was developed over a period of eight years and was broadly denounced as being excessively burdensome and complicated. Over the course of the last year, the Department of Labor conducted three major public forums around the country and met with scores of stakeholders, collecting hundreds of sets of written comments and taking testimony from 100 speakers, including organized labor, workers, medical experts, and businesses.

© MCMXCVII - MMXIII by www.mancomm.com

OSHA's Voluntary Ergonomic Guidelines

> OSHA announced its comprehensive plan to dramatically reduce ergonomic injuries on April 5, 2002. In addition to industry- and task-specific guidelines, the plan includes tough enforcement measures, workplace outreach, advanced research, and dedicated efforts to protect Hispanic and other immigrant workers.

> OSHA's approach to ergonomics is the development of industry and task-specific guidelines to reduce and prevent workplace ergonomic injuries called MSDs.

OSHA Guidelines

Musculoskeletal Disorders (MSDs)

What are MSDs?

> They are a group of physical conditions that involve the nerves, tendons, muscles, and spine, and they represent a wide range of disorders that can cause severe chronic and debilitating conditions such as:

>> carpal tunnel syndrome

>> swelling of the tendons

>> tension neck syndrome

>> low back pain

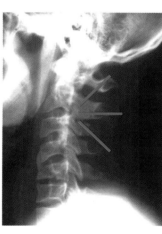

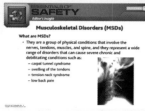

Editor's Insight

How common are MSDs?

> They are among the most prevalent medical problems—affecting 7% of the population and accounting for 14% of physician visits and 19% of hospital stays.

> In 2011, the Bureau of Labor Statistics reported over 387,800 occupational MSDs.

Bureau of Labor Statistics

What can be done to prevent work-related MSDs?

> Establish an ergonomics program, which can be tailored to a particular workplace.

> Perform work area hazard assessments to help identify jobs and tasks that can cause MSDs.

> When analyzing jobs or tasks that may be associated with MSDs, conditions to consider include:

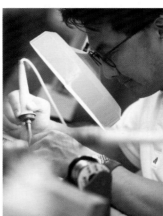

» awkward postures:

> prolonged work with hands above the head, elbows above the shoulders, or with the neck bent; squatting, kneeling, or lifting; handling objects with back bent or twisted; repeated or sustained bending or twisting of wrists, knees, hips, or shoulders; forceful and repeated gripping or pinching

» forceful lifting, pushing, or pulling:

> handling heavy objects; moving bulky or slippery objects

» prolonged repetitive motion:

> using a keyboard, tools, or knives; packaging, handling, or manipulating objects

» contact stress:

> repeated contact with hard or sharp objects, like desk or table edges

» vibration:

> overuse of power hand tools

© MCMXCVII - MMXIII by www.mancomm.com

What are possible ergonomic solutions?

> Adjust the height of working surfaces.

> Provide the right tool for the job.

> Add a platform.

> Provide mechanical lifting equipment.

> Provide ergonomic chairs or stools.

> Reposition tools or equipment.

> Pad hand tools and work surfaces.

> Provide foot rests.

> Change the size of grips or knobs.

> Use telephone headsets.

Office Ergonomics

See the "Desktop Computer Users Checklist" in your Student Workbook for some additional pointers on office ergonomics.

Neutral body positioning creates a comfortable working posture in which your joints are naturally aligned.

> Hands, wrists, and forearms are straight.

> Head is level or bent slightly forward.

> Shoulders are relaxed, and upper arms hang normally at the side of the body.

> Elbows stay close to the body.

> Feet are fully supported by the floor or a foot rest.

> Back is fully supported.

> Thighs and hips are supported.

> Knees are about the same height as the hips with the feet slightly forward.

Working with the body in a neutral position reduces stress and strain on the muscles, tendons, and skeletal system and reduces the risk of developing an MSD.

NIOSH Facts

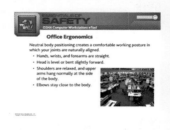

OSHA Computer Workstations eTool

Chairs

A good chair provides necessary support to the back, legs, buttocks, and arms.

Increased adjustability ensures a better fit for the user.

Desks

A well-designed and appropriately adjusted desk:

> provides adequate clearance for your legs;

> allows proper placement of computer components and accessories; and

> minimizes awkward postures and exertions.

Selecting and Arranging Desktop Components

Appropriate placement of the components and accessories for the desktop computer workstation allows you to work in neutral body positions.

Telephones

Telephones have cords that can get tangled up and can cause the user to assume awkward postures.

Placing the telephone too far away can cause you to repeatedly reach, resulting in strain on the shoulder, arm, and neck.

Prolonged conversations with the phone pinched between your shoulder and head may cause neck pain.

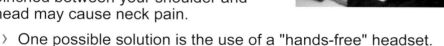

> One possible solution is the use of a "hands-free" headset.

© MCMXCVII - MMXIII by www.mancomm.com

Object Placement

Keyboards, pointing devices, or working surfaces that are too high or low can lead to awkward wrist, arm, and shoulder postures.

> One possible solution is to adjust the chair and work surface height to maintain a neutral body position.

Pointer/Mouse

To use a pointer or mouse in an ergonomically correct manner:

> Position the pointer/mouse to allow you to maintain a straight, neutral wrist posture.

> Keep the pointer/mouse close to the keyboard.

> Alternate hand used for operation.

> Use keyboard shortcuts to reduce extended use.

Office Environment

To create an ergonomically sound office environment:

> Arrange your office to minimize glare from overhead lights, desk lamps, and windows.

> Maintain proper air circulation.

> Avoid sitting directly under air conditioning vents that "dump" air right on top of you.

>> Temperatures above or below standard comfort levels can affect comfort and productivity.

> Ensure proper lighting, as follows:

>> Because bright lights shining on the display screen "wash out" images, and straining to view objects on the screen can lead to eye fatigue, remove the middle bulbs of 4-bulb fluorescent light fixtures to reduce brightness.

>> Because bright light sources behind the display screen create contrast problems, use blinds or drapes on windows to eliminate bright light

OSHA Computer Workstations eTool

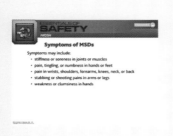

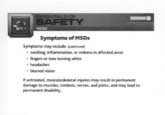

NIOSH

Symptoms of MSDs

Symptoms may include:

> stiffness or soreness in joints or muscles

> pain, tingling, or numbness in hands or feet

> pain in wrists, shoulders, forearms, knees, neck, or back

> stabbing or shooting pains in arms or legs

> weakness or clumsiness in hands

> swelling, inflammation, or redness in affected areas

> fingers or toes turning white

> headaches

> blurred vision

If untreated, musculoskeletal injuries may result in permanent damage to muscles, tendons, nerves, and joints, and may lead to permanent disability.

NIOSH Information

Carpal tunnel syndrome

> Carpal tunnel receives its name from the eight bones in the wrist, called carpals, which form a tunnellike structure. The tunnel is filled with flexor tendons that control finger movement. It also provides a pathway for the median nerve to reach sensory cells in the hand. Repetitive flexing and extension of the wrist may cause a thickening of the protective sheaths that surround each of the tendons. The swollen tendon sheaths, or tenosynovitis, apply increased pressure on the median nerve and produce carpal tunnel syndrome.

> As symptoms increase, tingling may develop during the day, commonly in the thumb, index, and ring fingers. A decreased ability and power to squeeze things may follow. Many patients with carpal tunnel syndrome are unable to differentiate hot from cold by touch, and experience an apparent loss of strength in their fingers. They appear clumsy because they have trouble performing simple tasks such as tying their shoes or picking up small objects.

© MCMXCVII - MMXIII by www.mancomm.com

Conclusion

Benefits of an Ergonomics Program

> Prevent injuries.

> Reduce worker compensation costs.

> Reduce OSHA-recordable injuries.

> Produce other benefits, including:

>> reduced fatigue and discomfort,

>> quality of work which means more productivity, and

>> quality of life for workers which can lead to better morale.

Discussion

Notes

© MCMXCVII - MMXIII by www.mancomm.com

Module Thirty-Seven
Medical Services and First Aid

regSMART™	Medical Services and First Aid
Scope	§1910.151
Management Controls	§1910.151
Alerts (postings, signs, markings)	
Records and Procedures	
Training	§1910.151(b)

Covers 1910.151

§1910.151(a), (b)

Medical Services and First Aid

Ensure that medical personnel are readily available for advice and consultation.

In the absence of an infirmary, clinic, or hospital in near proximity to the workplace that is used for the treatment of all injured employees:

> A person or persons shall be adequately trained to render first aid.

> Adequate first-aid supplies shall be readily available.

Safety STOP™ — OSHA Letter of Interpretation — 03/23/07: Bisland

Definition of "near proximity"

> In workplaces where serious accidents such as those involving falls, suffocation, electrocution, or amputation are possible, emergency medical services must be available within 3 — 4 minutes, if there is no employee on the site who is trained to render first aid.

> In workplaces, such as offices, where the possibility of such serious work-related injuries is less likely, a longer response time of up to 15 minutes may be reasonable.

Safety STOP™ — OSHA Letter of Interpretation — 04/18/02: Mateus

Employers should have a first-aid kit readily available.

> The term "readily available" is not defined in the standard. However, responding in a timely manner can mean the difference between life and death. Therefore, the person who has been trained to render first aid must be able to quickly access the first-aid supplies in order to effectively provide injured or ill employees with first-aid attention. The first-aid supplies should be located in an easily accessible area, and the first-aid provider generally should not have to travel through several doorways, hallways, and/or stairways to access first-aid supplies.

> As an employer would not know in advance whether a life-threatening injury would occur, an employer should not use the 15-minute (non-life-threatening) timeframe for determining the quantity and location of first-aid supplies; however, a 3-4 minute (life-threatening) timeframe would be acceptable.

© MCMXCVII - MMXIII by www.mancomm.com

Emergency Eyewash and Shower Requirements

Where the eyes or body of any person may be exposed to injurious corrosive materials, suitable facilities for quick drenching or flushing of the eyes and body shall be provided within the work area for immediate emergency use.

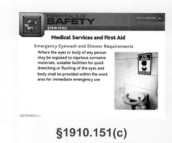

§1910.151(c)

™

Safety STOP

Safety Tip — ANSI Z358.1-1998 (Sections 4, 5, and 8)

Emergency eyewash and shower equipment
> Immediate emergency use means within 10-15 seconds with no obstructions to interfere with accessibility.
> Water flow rate requirements for emergency eyewash and shower equipment:
>> 15 minutes of continuous flush for eyewash at a rate of 0.4 gallons per minute
>> 20 gallons per minute for emergency showers

Editor's note: Don't forget to use the Safety Data Sheet to determine first-aid measures.

Notes

© MCMXCVII - MMXIII by www.mancomm.com

Module Thirty-Eight
Forklift Workshop

Case Studies

The following case studies are all incidents involving forklifts. After reviewing each case, discuss how this incident could be prevented from happening again in the future.

Case Study 1

The Incident:

A person was riding on the forks of a forklift as it approached an intersection. The forklift operator slowed down and turned his head to check for oncoming traffic. When he turned his head back, he could not see the person that was on the forks. He stopped the forklift and found out he had run over the worker, who was lying underneath the right side of the forklift.

Discussion for Case Study 1:

> What could prevent this incident from happening again?

Discussion

Discussion

Case Study 2

The Incident:

A wooden pallet was placed on top of the forks of a forklift, and a worker then stood on the pallet. The forklift operator raised the forks 16 feet above the concrete floor to the top of the storage rack. While the worker was placing a few tires on the pallet, the forklift operator noticed that the pallet was becoming unstable, but it was too late. The worker lost his balance and fell, striking his head on the floor.

Discussion for Case Study 2:

> What could prevent this incident from happening again?

Case Study 3

The Incident:

A forklift was traveling in reverse at high speed down an aisle when it hit a metal scrap bin, pushing it toward a punch press. Multiple impacts between the scrap bin, forklift, and press ultimately crushed the press operator.

Discussion for Case Study 3:

> What could prevent this incident from happening again?

© MCMXCVII - MMXIII by www.mancomm.com

Case Study 4

The Accident:

A 16-year-old worker drove a forklift from a warehouse to an outside storage yard. As he turned off an asphalt roadway onto the gravel surfaced storage yard, the forklift tipped over. The worker was not wearing a seat belt, and either jumped or was thrown from the operator's seat. The forklift tipped over on its side and the overhead guard pinned him to the ground, fatally crushing him.

Discussion for Case Study 4:

› What could prevent this incident from happening again?

Notes

© MCMXCVII - MMXII by www.mancomm.com

Credits

Module 21: Safety and Health Program
Conference center receives USACE safety inspection by USACE Europe District • http://www.flickr.com/photos/europedistrict/4884534393/

File Cabinets by grafixar • http://www.morguefile.com/archive/display/612479

Module 22: Emergency Action Plan
DSCF1441 by ronnieb • http://morguefile.com/archive/display/64524

Flash over by kilt medic • http://www.flickr.com/photos/20949260@N02/2191817720/

Project Vortex-99- Occluded mesocyclone tornado (NOAA_unidentified fotog) by pingnews.com • http://www.flickr.com/photos/pingnews/452392668/

Module 23: Sanitation
_MG_2855 by dlogue • http://www.morguefile.com/archive/display/785607

bathroom by Shifty

garbage_can2 by earl53 • http://morguefile.com/archive/display/108005

Locker room with lonely lab coat by jepoirrier • http://www.flickr.com/photos/jepoirrier/112132735/

PIC1083429620 by mensatic • http://www.morguefile.com/archive/display/15057

School cafeteria by Leo-setÃ¤ • http://www.flickr.com/photos/uncle-leo/4601491155/

shower by Shifty

wash by mensatic • http://www.morguefile.com/archive/display/595594

Module 24: Signs/Tags
114297235734 by rollingroscoe • http://morguefile.com/archive/display/111071

CGC Gallatin - Drydock by The MK Shop • http://www.flickr.com/photos/themkshop/3584297652/

MF_9048 by taliesin • http://morguefile.com/archive/display/184986

Tag-out by Beige Alert • http://www.flickr.com/photos/beigephotos/5297937550/

Module 25: Permit-Required Confined Spaces, Part 2
Brighton Sewer Tour by Dominic's pics • http://www.flickr.com/photos/64097751@N00/4001910196

Certified Industrial Hygienist Dan Napier at Confined Space Site by MargaretNapier • http://www.flickr.com/photos/marge__napier/4385403889/

confined space entry for installing flow monitoring equipment in the sewer at the combined sewer overflow point by Soggydan • http://www.flickr.com/photos/soggydan/3956358052/

confined space entry for installing flow monitoring equipment in the sewer at the combined sewer overflow point By Soggydan • http://www.flickr.com/photos/soggydan/3955579463/

Danger confined space by Pierre LaScott • http://www.flickr.com/photos/pierrelaphoto/114910942/

Demineralized water storage tank by gogogadgetscott • http://www.flickr.com/photos/gogogadgetscott/2198901198/

img_2456 by mlinksva • http://www.flickr.com/photos/mlinksva/4357495445/

img_2457 by mlinksva • http://www.flickr.com/photos/mlinksva/4357496181/

SORS confined space by iraxmas • http://www.flickr.com/photos/iraxmas/643462617/

Storage tank cleaning by Marc Taylor • http://www.flickr.com/photos/armyenvironmental/4417548442/

Untitled by Foxtongue • http://www.flickr.com/photos/foxtongue/2574118834/

Module 26: Lockout/Tagout, Part 2
hoover-5 by octal • http://www.flickr.com/photos/octal/286175703/

tag-in tag-out by a L p • http://www.flickr.com/photos/andyprice/1443593044/

Module 27: Welding/Cutting/Brazing
gascylinder_02 by GCPLearning • http://www.flickr.com/photos/gcplearning/4112845925/

Sailor arc-welds a flange aboard amphibious dock landing ship. by Official U.S. Navy Imagery • http://www.flickr.com/photos/usnavy/5505983253/

Sailor arc-welds a flange aboard USS Pearl Harbor. by Official U.S. Navy Imagery • http://www.flickr.com/photos/usnavy/5506578568/

Star Wars by Eneas • http://www.flickr.com/photos/eneas/2718318943/

techshop_members_welding_project by TechShop • http://www.flickr.com/photos/techshop/2832912619/

Vollgut by eriwst • http://www.flickr.com/photos/eriwst/3192010721/

Weld Class 11-1-08 by Photo Dudes • http://www.flickr.com/photos/photo-dudes/2992373991/

Welder on High Steel - San Francisco, California by gregor_y • http://www.flickr.com/photos/gregor_y/38137970/

Welding Pipe by 54034 • http://www.flickr.com/photos/54683320@N02/5522055516/

Module 28: Hand and Portable Power Tools
Drill by Josh and Melanie Rosenthal • http://www.flickr.com/photos/sensibleabode/306826721/

DSCN9828 by mtneer_man • http://www.flickr.com/photos/mtneer_man/4613789217/

Edge by Velo Steve • http://www.flickr.com/photos/juniorvelo/

Lawnmower by pambenn • http://morguefile.com/archive/display/96608

Let the Sparks Fly - Makita 9557NB Angle Grinder by toolstop • http://www.flickr.com/photos/toolstop/4071724564/

Let the Sparks Fly - The Makita 2414NB Abrasive Cut Off Saw by toolshop • http://www.flickr.com/photos/42408834@N06/4071720374

Susan Harwood Grant Number SH-17792-08-60-F-48 by Compacion Foundation

Module 29: Electrical Personal Protective Equipment
B7e47n 008 by duboix • http://www.morguefile.com/archive/display/676994

cohdra_100_0554 by cohdra • http://morguefile.com/archive/display/136560

hard hats by MichellLaurence • http://www.flickr.com/photos/55179598@N02/5164172229/

potential arc flash hazard by brionv • http://www.flickr.com/photos/brionv/374134849/

Module 31: Hazard Communication, Part 2
(SDSs)At National Prosthetics and Orthotics Boston by Nadya Peek • http://www.flickr.com/photos/nadya/4423260594/

Star Wars by Eneas • http://www.flickr.com/photos/eneas/2718318943/

Module 32: Industrial Hygiene
Conference center receives USACE safety inspection by USACE Europe District • http://www.flickr.com/photos/europedistrict/4885136304/

PIC1083429620 by mensatic • http://www.morguefile.com/archive/display/15057

Radiation Hazard by MountainAsh • http://www.flickr.com/photos/mountain-ash/2238824400/

Module 34: Hazardous Materials
dip_tank by Shifty

IMG_2255 by mconnors • http://www.morguefile.com/archive/display/569314

Module 35: Recordkeeping, Part 2
wetfloor by Shifty

Module 36: Ergonomics
DSCF1405 by ronnieb • http://morguefile.com/archive/display/65411

my desk, annotated by jimw • http://www.flickr.com/photos/jimwinstead/73973099/

Newsroom by victoriapeckham • http://www.flickr.com/photos/victoriapeckham/261126382/

Still bare, my office on 8th. by moriza • http://www.flickr.com/photos/moriza/57111960/

Module 37: Medical Services and First Aid
emergency shower_eye wash by peretzpup • http://www.flickr.com/photos/peretzpup/2403202007/

Notes

© MCMXCVII - MMXIII by www.mancomm.com

Index Vol II

© MCMXCVII - MMXIII by www.mancomm.com

© MCMXCVII - MMXIII by www.mancomm.com

Notes

© MCMXCVII - MMXIII by www.mancomm.com